NEWPORT PAGNELL'S BRIDGES

The Tickford Iron Bridge in Context

Tickford Bridge, from Castle Meadow, December 2008.

NEWPORT PAGNELL'S BRIDGES

The Tickford Iron Bridge in Context

Dennis C. Mynard

Paul Woodfield and Ray Bailey

PHILLIMORE

2009

Published by
PHILLIMORE & CO. LTD
Chichester, West Sussex, England
www.phillimore.co.uk
www.thehistorypress.co.uk

© Dennis C. Mynard, Paul Woodfield and Ray Bailey, 2009

ISBN 978-1-86077-603-8

Printed and bound in Malta

Contents

List of Illustrations

Front Endpaper: The town and rivers, based on the Ordnance Survey
                   map of c.1880.
Back Endpaper: Drawing of the Tickford Bridge by Paul Woodfield.

Acknowledgements

In particular we are indebted to the staff of the Buckinghamshire County Record Office and to Ruth Meardon of the Milton Keynes Local Studies Centre for assistance with research. The report by the Buckinghamshire County Council Bridge Inspector, P.J. Peters, was an invaluable help with details of recent work on the bridge.

The following people also helped in various ways with research into surviving and lost iron bridges: Nick Crank of the Milton Keynes Historic Environment Record; Debra Francis, librarian; Carol Morgan, archivist at the Institution of Civil Engineers; Paul J. Sedgewick and Pauline Cross regarding the Stratfield Saye Bridge; Luke Skerrit and Polly Stanley, collections officers, Boston Borough Council; Boston Reference Library; Colin Johnson, archivist, Bath and North Somerset County Council; and the Sunderland City Council, Local Collection archivist.

Others that have helped are Michael O'Sullivan for information on the Pont des Arts, Paris, and Barry Clayton of Tyringham for details of Henry Provis and his long association with North Bucks. We are also indebted to Allan Burnett, civil engineer, for reading drafts of Paul's work and suggesting very welcome improvements, and finally, Gerald Stratton, for reading and editing part of the book.

Many of the photographs in this book are from the Ray Bailey collection; others were provided by Paul Woodfield, 9, 11-13, 20-1, 23-4, 26, 28-9; *The Bucks Herald*, 35-7; Dennis Mynard, 7, 30, 32-3, 39; Maurice Barratt, 30; John Mitchell, 19; Newport Pagnell Historical Society, 40; The Bath City Archive, 25; and The Guildhall Museum and Art Gallery, Boston, 14-15; and the late Howard Norfolk and Aquarticles, Vancouver, Canada, 10.

Finally, we acknowledge a generous grant towards publication from H.W. Mason and Sons of Newport Pagnell and Milton Keynes, the oldest established builders and funeral directors in the area, and an advance from the Harry Middleton Trust, which also represents an old Newport Pagnell family. Without their support this book might not have been published.

CONVENTIONS

Throughout this book all dimensions are given in feet and inches in preference to metric figures; imperial notation was used by the engineers and designers at the time. Similarly, monetary references are in the original pounds, shillings and pence.

Introduction

The year 2010 is an important one for Newport Pagnell, as the town's bridges celebrate their bicentenary. The Tickford Bridge, a Scheduled Ancient Monument of international importance, was based on a design by Thomas Wilson and Rowland Burdon, and was cast by Messrs Walker of Rotherham in 1810; the abutments were designed by Henry Provis.

Tickford Bridge is the oldest surviving cast-iron bridge in the western hemisphere which carries everyday traffic on a main road. The idea that the town should celebrate the bicentenary of the Tickford, or 'Iron Bridge' as it is known locally, was proposed by local resident Roy Mason, and subsequently the Tickford Bridge Bicentenary Committee was established to promote the event.

Dennis Mynard was requested to write a history of the Iron Bridge, the publication of which will precede the bicentenary in 2010. Dennis decided not to limit the book to the story of the Tickford Bridge alone. He felt that it should deal with both of the town's bridges, which were rebuilt in 1809-10, subsequent to an Act of Parliament passed in 1809. The Act was specifically for the rebuilding and widening of both the North and Tickford bridges and their approach roads.

Therefore, whilst the Tickford Bridge is the principal subject, this book relates the history of the town's bridges from the earliest times to the present day, and discusses the Iron Bridge in detail. The text is the work of Dennis, with two other local historians, Ray Bailey and Paul Woodfield, becoming involved in the process at his request. Ray has carried out extensive research and made a photographic record of the Bridge Trustees Minute Books, Account Books, and other documents at the Buckinghamshire County Record Office, Gomme's Forge and the *Bucks Herald*, enabling Dennis to research them without travelling from Norfolk to Aylesbury. Paul, a Historic Buildings Specialist, is the author of Chapter Six, and his contribution places the Tickford Bridge in the context of other cast-iron bridges and provides details of its construction in Chapter Seven.

I

The Town and its First Bridges

Newport was established during the late ninth century in a strategic, elevated position overlooking the confluence and crossing points of the Rivers Ouse and Lovat. At that time the upper Ouse Valley was in the borderland between the Saxon and Danish areas of the country. A treaty of A.D. 886 agreed by King Alfred with the Danes allowed trade between the Danes and the Saxons. However, incursions by the Danes into the borderland area led to both Buckingham and Bedford towns being fortified in A.D. 915. It is likely that at Newport a minor defensive position was also established, commanding the crossings of the rivers Ouse and Lovat.

The trading settlement which grew up west of this fortified area was given the name 'Newport', meaning 'New Town' or 'Market'. The addition of 'Pagnell' to the name was derived from the Paganell family, Lords of the Manor in the late 11th and early 12th centuries. The town became an important trading centre; Saxon pennies with the mint mark 'NIPEPORT' are thought to have been produced here before A.D. 973.

Newport soon incorporated 'Ticheford', a settlement on the south side of the river Lovat, first recorded in the Domesday Survey of 1086. The name is derived from the ford over the river. The first element of the settlement name comes from 'Ticcen', the name for a young 'kid' goat. Animal names were often associated with fords.

The ford was an important river crossing on the road from London to Bedford, Northampton and beyond, and also for local people to bring their produce into the town's market. Due to the town's strategic location, the safety of the river crossing points and the market was ensured. Timber bridges soon stood alongside the fords and were later rebuilt in stone. The medieval town had two bridges, the North Bridge over the Ouse and the South Bridge over the Lovat. The latter, sometimes referred to as the 'Newport Bridge', soon became known as the 'Tickford Bridge'.

THE TICKFORD BRIDGE

Remains of wooden posts found when the abutments for the Iron Bridge were constructed confirm that the first bridge on the site was built of timber. The earliest known documentary reference to this bridge is from a charter granted to the monks of Tickford Priory confirming their lands. Dating from *c.*1175-80, the charter mentions 'the meadow situate between the bridge of Newport and the house of the monks'. After a disastrous fire destroyed the Priory's records, a new charter, confirming its lands and possessions, was granted in 1311 by Edward II. This new charter contains the first known reference to 'The Bridge of Tykford'. From then on the bridge, often mentioned in legal documents, was generally called 'Tickford Bridge', and occasionally the 'South Bridge'.

Precisely when the bridge was rebuilt in stone is unknown, but it was most likely to have been in the 1380s, when money for bridge repairs was provided by King Richard II. This bridge survived until 1810. A directory of 1790 recorded that when entering the town from the London Road, 'You cross the river Lovat by a strong stone bridge'.

THE NORTH BRIDGE

The road running north from the town originally crossed the Ouse at two fording points: one across the main river, now at the bottom of Ousebank gardens, locally known as Brooklands, and the other across an old course in Lathbury parish.

The first North Bridge, situated just upstream of the ford, was timber-built and replaced, probably *c.*1380, by a stone bridge of three arches which survived until the building of the present bridge in 1810. One arch of the medieval bridge can still be seen on the south side of the present North Bridge in Ousebank Gardens.

After the first North Bridge was built over the main stream of the Ouse, the road continued, running on a low causeway across the flood meadows to the ford in Lathbury. This was always a difficult and dangerous crossing, liable to flooding. In times of flood a ferry was used to carry carts and coaches over.

2

The Medieval Stone Bridges: Perilous Crossings for Travellers

From the earliest times the low-lying land alongside the Ouse was submerged at times of flood. The road from Newport Pagnell to Lathbury is raised on a low embankment which must have been put in place at an early date. Similarly, the road from the town to Sherington Bridge is also raised above the level of the adjacent meadows.

In times of flood, Newport would almost have appeared to be on the coast. Perhaps this is the reason for the public house standing next to the old North Bridge being called the *Ship* in the 17th century; the name was later changed to the *Neptune*.

The bridges needed to be kept in good condition, and their maintenance became the responsibility of the burgesses and tradesmen in the town. They were, however, in poor condition by 1380 when the men of the town, unable to afford repairs, were granted a Royal Grant of Pontage by Richard II, which empowered them to levy a tax on travellers using the bridges for a period of three years to raise money for repair of the town's bridges. The Grant was made to leading townsmen Thomas Cowe, Robert Bewes, John Taillour and Simon Sweet, and was to be repaid to the king from the toll charges levied.

A further Grant in the following year, to the same men, probably resulted in the old timber bridges being replaced with stone. This charter confirmed the collecting of tolls as below:

> Know ye that in aid of the mending and repairing of the bridges of North Brigge and South Brigge in the town of Newport Pagnell which are broken and injured to the grievous damage and danger of the men crossing by the said bridges and for the mending and repairing whereof the men of the said town are from year to year as we understand heavily charged, we have, by our special grace, granted to you that from the day of making these presents up to the end of three years following fully to be completed you may take by the hands of those whom you trust, and for

whom you are willing to answer, of things saleable passing over and under the said bridges the customs underwritten namely:

For every horse load of corn one farthing,
For every cartload of corn one halfpenny,
For every horse mare ox and cow one farthing,
For every horseload of cloth one halfpenny,
For every whole cloth one farthing,
For every hundredweight of linen cloth canvas cloths of Ireland, Galewath and Worstede one halfpenny,
For every cask of wine or cineres one halfpenny,
For every cartload of honey one halfpenny,
For every bundle of cloth brought by a cart twopence,
For every hundredweight of avoirdupois one penny,
For every weight of tallow and grease one farthing,
For every quarter of wood one halfpenny,
For every hundredweight of alum, copperas, clay and verdegrease one farthing,
For every two thousand weight of tallow one farthing,
For ten bundles of garlic one farthing,
For every thousand herrings one farthing,
For every cartload of sea fish one penny,
For every horseload of sea fish one farthing,
For every hundredweight of planks one halfpenny,
For every millstone one farthing,
For every quarter of salt one farthing,
For every weight of cheese or butter one farthing,
For every cartload of wood or charcoal one farthing,
For every quarter of oak bark one farthing,
For every bundle of any merchandise above the sum of five shillings one farthing,
For every hundredweight of tin brass and copper one halfpenny,
For every hundredweight of bundles of steel one farthing. For every other thing of the value of five shillings not here specified crossing over and under the said bridges, wool, leather, hides, and also iron and lead whilst taxed excepted, one farthing.

And therefore we command you that you take the said customs until the end of three years and apply them towards the repair and mending of the said bridges, as is aforesaid, but when the term of the said three years is completed the said customs shall entirely cease and be discontinued.

The tolls were applicable only to goods which were on sale, or were to be sold. These were the first of several Royal Grants made to the town for bridge repairs. During the 15th century the townsmen assumed responsibility for the care of the bridges through the Guilds of St Mary and St John. Eventually, an appointed group of leading townsmen, known as the 'Feoffees of the Town Lands and Tenements', became responsible for the upkeep and repair of the bridges and other properties.

Local benefactors now began to bequeath property to the Feoffees; this became their main source of income. One such benefactress was Beatrice Halliday, a widow who, in 1499, bequeathed the *Bell*, later known as the *Red Lion*, and two closes, one in Fisher's Weeke and the other adjoining Bury Field, towards the maintenance of the Bridge of Newport Pagnell, mending of the highways, mending of the Parish Church and the relief of the poor. Beatrice's daughter confirmed the gift in 1524.

In 1559 Thomas Childs left a house in Tickford End, near Tickford Bridge, towards the repair of the bridge. In 1598 an inquisition was held concerning this property because the ownership of the house was questioned, and it noted that 'the rent had been employed about the same bridge till now.'

Over the next three centuries the wills of many local people included bequests of property or money for the maintenance of the bridges.

3

The Coaching Trade in the Eighteenth and Nineteenth Centuries

Coach travel throughout the country became easier in the 18th century, as roads were improved by the creation of Turnpike Trusts. Acts of Parliament also enabled local businessmen and wealthy landowners to form Trusts to repair and improve certain roads, the work being paid for by the collection of tolls once the road had been improved. These roads, each with their own Toll Houses, became known as 'Turnpike Roads'. Travellers to Newport Pagnell left Watling Street at Hockliffe and proceeded to the town of Woburn. This road was turnpiked as early as 1706, and extended to Newport in 1728. The road from Northampton to Stoke Goldington was thus improved in 1708, and the length from Stoke Goldington to Newport Pagnell was turnpiked in 1723. Further Acts of Parliament provided for improvements to the road through Olney to Wellingborough and Kettering in 1754, and the roads to Bedford in 1814 and to Buckingham in 1815.

The town's Feoffees did not always have sufficient income to maintain the bridges, and in 1720 and 1721 they were presented at the Manorial Court for not keeping them in repair.

The crossing of the Ouse was improved in the 1730s when a bridge was built in Lathbury parish by the Rev. William Symes, son-in-law of Henry Andrewes of Lathbury Manor. The stone for this bridge probably came from quarries at Quarry Hall Farm in Lathbury, and the gravel was dug near the bridge in a field between the Lathbury and Sherington roads, now called the 'Osier Cob'. The Lathbury Bridge had a locked gate at either end and it was opened mainly in times of flood when the ford near the bridge was impassable. A toll was charged for crossing the bridge at these times.

A glimpse of travelling at this time is afforded by the following announcement taken from the *Northampton Mercury* of 10 October 1743:

On Monday the 24th of this Instant October, at Three o'clock in the Morning will set out (and continue so to do) from the *White Lyon* in Northampton, a good and Neat Ge-hoe Coach, with six Able Horses (which will with Ease and Pleasure carry eight Persons) and will be at the *Ram Inn* in Smithfield, London, every Tuesday early in the Afternoon: returns on Wednesday about ten o'clock, and will be in Northampton on Friday afternoon.

Every passenger to London paying 7s., and from London to Northampton 6s., Being allowed fourteen Pounds weight and for all above as well as for other goods as usual. Performed (if God permit) by Robert Herbert. Passengers being ready at Newport Pagnell by ten o'clock may be taken in there. Note also, plate, money, writings, or jewels will not be answered for unless notice be given thereof.

An advertisement in the *Northampton Mercury* of the same date stated that carriers could purchase tickets for passing over the new Lathbury Bridge at Mr Gatfield's *The Stag's Head*, in Lathbury. A record of the toll fees taken from 1750-7 shows an average income of almost £40 a year.

To improve conditions for the increasing traffic on the road, the County Magistrates purchased the Lathbury Bridge in 1757 from Mrs Symes, the owner of Lathbury Manor. It was then thrown open to all travellers – soon afterwards

1   *Lathbury Bridge with a coach crossing the ford, 1798. From a drawing by J. Walker.*

the bridge was partly rebuilt in brick, widened, and a higher causeway erected on the Newport side to carry the road to it. The stone arches of the original bridge are still visible under the later brickwork.

Writing in 1783, William Bray recorded the Lathbury Bridge as follows:

> At the entrance to Newport Pagnell a causeway has been thrown up and a bridge built in a place which used to be impassable in floods except by a bridge belonging to a private person.

He noted that the horse path over the ford was always open and the carriage way over the bridge was only open when there was a flood.

A deep pit next to the Lathbury Bridge was named 'Packman's Pit', after a traveller and his load went into it during an exceptionally high flood. The print of 1798 (Fig. 1), shows the Lathbury Bridge of three arches, with Packman's Pit marked by fencing between the bridge and the ford. The text with the print stated the town was at the time 'situated between the river Ouse and another small stream over each of which is a large stone bridge. The country hereabouts is frequently flooded and the town has recently suffered considerable damage.'

By the end of the 18th century the number of coaches using the road had increased considerably; two coaches a day came from London. One left the *Bull and Mouth Inn*, Bull and Mouth Street, every morning at 6 a.m., Sunday excepted, and arrived in Newport at around 3 p.m. Another coach left *Blossoms Inn*, Lawrence Lane, at the same time. The fare was 10s. 6d. per person.

Many other coaches passed through the town, including the Leeds, Manchester, Nottingham, Derby, Leicester, Sheffield, and Holyhead. The Leeds, Chester, and Manchester mail coaches also passed through, along with the *Wellingborough Diligence*. Goods were carried by wagons to London from Newport Pagnell and Hanslope. Wagons, run by Thomas Rogers, set out from Newport every Wednesday and Saturday evening at 6 p.m. and arrived at the *Windmill Inn*, St John's Street, London, on the following Friday and Monday mornings at 4 a.m. The wagons returned on the same days at noon and arrived at Newport on Monday and Thursday mornings at 8 a.m.

The main inns in the town, for the accommodation of travellers, were the *Swan*, the *Saracen's Head* and *The George*, although the latter was principally a wagon inn. *The Stag's Head Inn*, Lathbury, also accommodated travellers, though an unfortunate fire in 1796 destroyed the stables and 25 horses died.

The bridges were gradually deteriorating; their repair was the responsibility of the town through the Feoffees of the Town Lands, whose early Account Books contain the following references to expenditure and work on the bridges. In 1801, Mr Beaty was paid £2 4s. for gravel to be spread on the North Bridge roadway. Subsequently, 65 loads of stone were laid on the bridge at a cost of £6 10s. The same year, William Rose was paid for laying stones at the foot of Tickford Bridge, and in September 5s. was paid for cleaning the bridge. The bridge work was an ongoing job; in February and March 1802, Edward Petts spent 14 days working on the bridge, and a Mr Battams and others were paid for laying stones.

Work on both bridges continued and in 1804 more stone was required, and work was carried out by a mason on the North Bridge. During the year, 30 loads of stone and an unknown quantity of beer was supplied to workmen on both bridges. The origin of some of the stones, which were probably mainly gravel, appears to have been Bury Field, for in 1805 Thomas Coles was paid for digging stones there. An unusual entry in the Account Books was payment to men for two days' work breaking the ice at the bridges in 1808.

These entries give an insight into the continuous programme of maintenance and repair required to keep the bridges open.

A faster coach service from Northampton to London was advertised in June 1804, in the *Northampton Mercury* as follows:

Northampton and Newport Pagnell
Elegant Light Coach
Upon an entire new principle
For four insides and three outsides

Now offered to the Public by Messrs Willan and Levi, Proprietors of the old Northampton Coach, Commenced on Monday the 25th inst from Northampton, and from London on Tuesday the 26th: to start precisely at seven in the morning, and will continue every other Day (till another of the Kind can be provided) *as follows* –

From Mr Levi's office, Gold Street, Northampton, on Mondays, Wednesdays and Fridays and from the *Bull and Mouth Inn*, Bull and Mouth Street London on Tuesdays, Thursdays, and Saturdays at the same hour.

To have one coachman only throughout the Journey and to stop at no place on the road, except for the purpose of changing horses; by which means the passengers will arrive in good time for dinner.

Inside fare 15s. and outside 9s.

N.B. The old Coach every morning as usual.

Whilst the Turnpike Trustees kept the roads in good condition they had no responsibility for the bridges which crossed the rivers at Newport. Throughout the century the crossing of the Ouse was a major problem in times of bad weather and flooding. A particularly bad accident on the North Bridge in January 1809 was reported in the *Northampton Mercury*:

> Early yesterday morning the Defiance Manchester Stage coach on its way from London was overturned upon the North Bridge, Newport Pagnell. From the overflowing of the water, in consequence of the thaw and the great rapidity of the current, several large holes had been washed out of the bridge, but at the time of the accident were entirely imperceptible, so that no blame can possibly attach to the Coach-Man. The passengers three inside escaped with no material injury. Joseph Keates Esq. of Cheapside was the only person hurt, who received a slight concussion to the head. The coach-man and guard though precipitated into the stream fortunately escaped without harm other than a complete ducking. This very narrow escape is another alarming proof of the absolute and immediate necessity of adopting the only efficient means of obviating similar accidents on one of the most crowded roads to the British Metropolis, namely building and widening both the bridges on an improved plan.

The dangerous state of the bridges was entirely caused by the town's inability to repair them due to lack of funds. However, their upkeep was essential since both the town and its immediate area were largely dependent on employment related to the coaching trade. The roads were an economic lifeline which was being strangled by the dilapidated and unsafe condition of the bridges.

Local businessmen were now seeking financial aid from the Government. As a result the *Northampton Mercury* concluded its report on the January accident with the following:

> We feel highly gratified in being able to announce that such a plan – with an estimate has been taken and a subscription set on foot and that immediate application will be made to Parliament for that purpose, under the auspices of a Committee of the most respected gentlemen of the town and the three hundreds of Newport, to whose laudable exertions we are happy to pay this tribute of applause.

The application to Parliament was successful.

4

Rebuilding the Town's Bridges: The Act of Parliament, 1809

An Act of Parliament for 'taking down and rebuilding parts of the North Bridge & Tickford Bridge and for widening the bridges & approaches thereto' was applied for, quickly passed, and gained Royal Assent in June 1809.

The Act stated that the bridges were ancient and decayed and, in consequence of the violence of recent floods, were so damaged as to be dangerous to travellers, carriages and cattle passing over them. The Act also noted that the roads approaching and travelling over the bridges were in many parts narrow, unsafe and incommodious.

The inhabitants of Newport Pagnell, although liable for the repair of the bridges, had insufficient funds to do so. The Act recommended that the bridges should in part be taken down and rebuilt, altered, and widened, stating that this would be a considerable advantage and benefit to the inhabitants of the town, travellers to it, and also the general public.

THE APPOINTMENT OF TRUSTEES TO REBUILD THE BRIDGES

The Act proposed the appointment of Trustees to oversee the rebuilding the bridges, and named 27 individuals selected mainly from the local gentry, landowners, clergymen and businessmen. The Trustees were: William Praed, Mansell Dawkin Mansell, Henry Hugh Hoare, Edward Watts, Philip Hoddle Ward, John Higgins the elder, John Higgins the younger, Charles Pinfold, Rev. Alexander Cromleholme, Rev. Primatt Knapp, Rev. James Meakin, Rev. John Wynter, Rev. William Smith, Rev. Robert Lowndes, Rev. Richard Cautley, Rev. Thomas Palmer Bull, Rev. Joseph Ward, Thomas Sanders Hollingworth, Isaac Henley Hanscomb, Charles Marius Hardy, Robert Jee, Thomas Meacher, John Chibnall, William Lucas, Joseph Cripps, Edward Jefferson, and George Osborn.

In order to take office, the Bridge Trustees had to swear an oath that he in his own right, or that of his wife, was in the actual possession or enjoyment of rents and profits from lands or tenements of the clear yearly value of £30, or to a personal estate with their wife of £1,000.

The Trustees could appoint a Treasurer, Clerk, a Collector of Tolls, surveyors of the bridges and any other officers that they required. They were given the authority to purchase property and land required for the erection of the new bridges. Properties in private ownership, that the Trustees would need to purchase and demolish to make way for the new bridges and the approach roads, were listed in the Act. The Trustees also had the authority to demolish all, or parts, of the existing bridges.

The Trustees were empowered to appoint contractors for the purchase of all materials required, and to employ workmen to carry out the work. Their surveyors had authority to dig, gather or take away stone, gravel, sand, earth or other materials out of, or from, any common or waste ground, river or brook in the parish, or any adjoining parish, town or hamlet without paying for the same. The surveyors were to backfill all quarries or pits dug, or fence them off for safety.

In the first instance, the whole project was to be financed by loans, the Trustees being authorised to borrow up to £12,000 from subscribers who would be paid interest every half a year from the income received from the tolls. The Act also listed property and lands in Newport Pagnell belonging to the Feoffees of the Town Lands, some of which had originally been bequeathed to them to provide money for the repair of the bridges. The Feoffees were ordered to pay such income to the Bridge Trustees, to be put towards the building of the new bridges.

The Trustees were authorised to build one or more Toll Houses, with gates across the roads at, or near, the end of the bridges, and to take tolls from all persons in respect of beasts, carriages, wagons and carts that passed over the bridges. The income from the tolls was to be used initially to pay the costs, charges and expenses incurred in obtaining the Act of Parliament; then the fees of surveyors etc. were to be paid; then the cost of building the new bridges and Toll Houses and widening the approach roads; and finally the subscribers were to be repaid.

The first meeting of the Trustees was to be held at the *Swan Hotel* on the third Tuesday after the passing of the Act, between the hours of 11 a.m. and 3 p.m., for the purpose of carrying the Act into execution.

The meeting duly took place at the *Swan* on Tuesday 27 June 1809 at 11 a.m. The nominated Trustees were elected; each had to swear the oath relating to their financial status, and that they would execute the duty of a Trustee given to them by the Act. William Lucas was appointed as the Clerk and Treasurer.

In addition to those named in the Act, the following were also elected and swore the Oath:

> William Henry Hanmer, George Lucas, W.B. Kilpin, George Cooch, William Levi, John Rogers, James Beard, Rev. W.B. Bull, Rev. George Morley, George Osborn Rogers, Robert Collison, Charles Redden.

After discussion, the Trustees all agreed that a new bridge should be built at, or near, the North Bridge, before the repair of the Tickford Bridge took place. However, any necessary repairs to the Tickford Bridge were to be carried out immediately. It was then resolved that a competent surveyor should be appointed to report on the existing bridges and to prepare a plan for rebuilding.

THE BUILDING OF THE NEW BRIDGES

No detailed record of the progress of the work on the bridges survives. The following account of the building of the bridges is based on information gleaned from the Trustees' Minute and Account Books.

When completed, the opening of the bridges was not formally celebrated and therefore dates have had to be deduced from the Account Books which record the commencement of the collection of tolls. Some information has also been gleaned from the work of earlier historians.

5
Building the North Bridges, 1809

Before earthmoving and building could start, the Bridge Trustees had to acquire several properties which were to be demolished to make way for the works, and they also needed to obtain the land on which the new bridge was to be built.

The old road ran down from the High Street, past Miss Charlotte Beaty's house (now the Royal British Legion Club), through the present Ousebank Gardens and over the old medieval bridge of three arches, one of which fortunately still survives. Miss Beaty's garden included land called 'The Knowl', 'The Island', and a shrubbery which she had purchased from the Lord of the Manor only two years earlier in 1808.

On the left of the old road going out of town were several properties, including a public house – all of these were to be purchased and demolished to make way for a road to the new bridge, which was to be erected alongside the old one. Beyond the new bridge, a newer three-arch bridge (now the middle bridge going out of town), was also built in a meadow called the 'Shoulder of Mutton'. Parts of an adjoining meadow, called 'Hog Holme', were also required.

John Walker, a farmer in Tickford End and a dealer in wood and coal, had a brick kiln on his land. Walker was appointed as surveyor and given the task of locating local sources of stone and other suitable materials which would be required for the rebuilding or repair of the North Bridge. Within a week he had located a good source of stone in a Close called the 'Sallage Pasture', on the Kickles Farm, which was occupied by John Cooper, and he was authorised to commence extracting stone and materials for the proposed work.

For the design of the bridges the Trustees agreed to consult Henry Provis, who had been the Senior Site Supervisor for the construction of Tyringham House for the architect Sir John Soane, 1793-1802, and subsequently the District Engineer of the Grand Junction Canal Company. Provis and a surveyor,

Mr Nixon, were invited to the third meeting of the Trustees on 4 July 1809. After discussion, Nixon was requested to prepare plans and an estimate of costs for making and forming three arches of 20-foot span and 24-foot width, and one arch of 40-foot span, and also for making the causeway and embankment walls and other work about the bridges.

Plans produced by Provis and Nixon were presented to the Trustees on 14 July 1809. Their proposals were for the new North Bridge and consisted of four arches carrying a raised roadway across the Ouse and its meanders. One arch of 40-foot span and 24-foot width in the clear between the walls was to be

2   *The original east face of the North Bridge,
built in 1809.*

made in the Meadow called 'Hog Holme', over the main stream of the river on the west side of the old North Bridge.

Two other arches of 20-foot span and 24-foot width in the clear were to be made in the Shoulder of Mutton meadow, and another arch of the same size between the first and the last mentioned arches was to be sited, at the discretion of Provis, in a place according to Nixon's plan. These three 20-foot arches (*see* Fig. 5) form the middle bridge, just past the Toll House on the way out of town, which was designed to carry excess flood water. The Trustees were happy with this design and Nixon was paid £29 12s. 6d. for his work. For some reason he received a further payment of £5 18s. 6d. in 1813.

Provis produced estimates, which were approved by the Trustees, for the cost of building the arches, causeway and embankments, parapets, and other work necessary to complete the proposed bridge. During July, Provis surveyed and set out the foundations of the arches. By August, John Crament had been appointed as Superintendent of Works, with instructions to let the digging for the foundations at a rate not exceeding 8d. per square yard for the excavation and first run, and not exceeding 2d. a yard for every other run.

The Trustees then purchased properties near the old North Bridge, which were required to be demolished before work could take place. As the project got underway it was agreed that a sub-committee of Trustees be formed to liaise with the Superintendent. The daily rates of pay to the workers on the bridge were as follows: 4s. to Master Masons; 3s. 6d. to Journeymen Masons; and 2s. each to labourers per day. As the work needed to continue during the winter it was agreed that the workmen who, after 16 September, were content with their wages would be employed during the winter in preference to others.

Nixon produced his estimate for making centres for the arches, but at £500 16s. 7d. it was considered too expensive and was rejected. A cheaper price for the same work was tendered by a Mr Swepston. He offered to make the four centres, three of 20 feet each, and one of 40-foot span, for £180. His plans and price were agreed and it was decided that he was to be paid £50 on erecting the first center, subject to his work being acceptable. After Swepston had completed his work on the wooden centers for the arches he claimed an extra £40 due to a deviation from his original contract. The Trustees disagreed and only paid him £20. However, he continued to work for them, later building a work shed and the first temporary Toll House at the North Bridge.

Work was now proceeding at a rate which demanded more stone and other materials. To keep up with demand, John Walker, the surveyor, obtained a pit in Ashway Hill Close in the Portfield, in the occupation of Joseph Hill. Several payments are recorded in the accounts, made to local contractors Joseph Hill and John Coles, for carrying stone and other materials. Blacksmiths, ironmongers and others also feature in these accounts. One of the Trustees, Mansell Dawkin Mansell, a land owner and farmer of Lathbury, supplied implements and materials.

A typical monthly account approved by the Trustees was entered in the Minute Books on 5 September 1809 as follows:

At meeting held this day the Auditors presented a report on the following accounts:

Mr William Atkins, farmer	£7	10	0
Luke Price, farrier	£9	1	10
Thomas Forster	£16	12	6
Joseph Hill for carriage of			
Stone and Materials	£73	9	5
John Walker for Lime	£24	15	0
John Buckby, miller	£19	15	1¼
Thomas Kilpin, ironmonger		6	0
" " for Grindstone		8	0
Mark Taylor, wheelwright		17	8
Jarvis	£14	17	11
John Coles for carrying			
Stone etc.	£30	0	0
M.D. Mansell for			
Implements materials etc.	£24	12	9¼
	£222	6	2½

By October 1809 the new three-arch middle bridge was completed, with a brick parapet wall 14 inches wide on either side. It was now time for the temporary bridge, as planned by Provis, to be erected to provide a roadway from the old North Bridge to the new three-arch bridge. At this stage it was proposed that the old bridge should be removed. However, the Trustees ruled that no part of it should be taken down unless absolutely necessary.

As soon as the temporary bridge was open, a Toll Gate was erected on the roadway, just past Miss Beaty's house. John Crament, the Superintendent of Works, now became the Keeper of the Gate and was paid one guinea per week. Whilst the temporary bridge was in use, a reduced rate of tolls was charged (*see* Appendix One). On Sundays, travellers paid double the normal rate. Tolls were

3 *Eroded keystones on the west face of the North Bridge, 1809, and in 1890 after widening.*

collected from 11 December 1809, and in the six months up to 7 June 1810, some £376 17s. was taken.

The North Bridge (*see* Fig. 4) was completed late in 1809, and carries the date (*see* Fig. 3) on the keystone of the arch, on its west face. Work on the bridges and the road connecting them was completed in the summer of 1810, a new Toll House was erected between them and full tolls were to be charged as soon as the road was opened. Local people were concerned about having to pay every time that they crossed the bridge; therefore, in September 1810, Mr William Atkins of Lathbury proposed to compound with the Trustees for the tolls payable, by himself and four other inhabitants or occupiers of land in Lathbury, at the sum of six guineas per annum for two years. Once the Tickford Bridge was opened, the same arrangement was made with residents of other local villages.

Now that the North Bridge was completed, local brewer and publican, Charles Redden, built a new public house opposite Miss Beaty's house, once again using the name *The Neptune*. Redden successfully applied for a continuation of the former Right of Way from his yard to the river, and also for a carriage way from the bridge to his yard.

The old *Neptune*, now derelict and partly demolished, was trapped between a new roadside wall and Miss Beaty's garden; so Redden sold it to her in December 1810. Miss Beaty, wishing to tidy up after the bridge builders, applied to purchase the old road and the remaining arch of the old bridge (*see* Fig. 7) from the Trustees. This raised an interesting problem for the Trustees, and they considered seeking the opinion of the Attorney General as to whether the site of the old bridge was vested in them under the Act of Parliament. If so, the

4   *The west face of the widened North Bridge.*

5   *The Middle Bridge. The three stone arches show the iron corbels added when the bridge was widened in 1890.*

Trustees questioned whether they had the right to sell the land upon which the old bridge and the route of the old road stood.

This question was eventually resolved, however, and by October 1811 Miss Beaty acquired the old road, the remains of the bridge, and part of the bed of the old river, and she added them to her garden; now Ousebank public gardens.

The traveller, John Hassel, writing in 1819, described the town's new bridges as follows:

> That over the Ouse, called North Bridge, may rather be considered a series of bridges, connected with each other by high mounds of earth, inclosed between strong stone walls, built after the manner of Vauban (Military Earthworks in France) over which the road is carried. The whole breadth of waterway of this bridge is 200 feet, and the largest arch is 40 feet; the stone of which it is built is a hard limestone, found in the parish of Newport Pagnell, about a mile from the town. The foundations are built on a solid rock, twelve feet below the surface of the river.

6   *(Above Right) The Toll House on the North Bridge.*

7   *(Right) The remaining arch of the medieval North Bridge.*

6

The Tickford Iron Bridge in Context

At Newport Pagnell, the Trustees empowered to build the town's new bridges included a local parson, the Rev. Richard Cautley of Moulsoe. In late 1809, the Rev. Cautley made a journey to Sunderland, County Durham, to study the world-famous Iron Bridge, designed by Thomas Wilson in collaboration with Rowland Burdon. There he met both gentlemen and was able to report back his findings to his Newport Pagnell committee.

Cast-iron bridges were now becoming fashionable, and the trustees, anxious to improve the town, entrusted Walkers of Rotherham to cast the new bridge over the Lovat at Newport Pagnell. Walkers had already cast many bridges (Appendix Three), and the Tickford Bridge, designed by Thomas Wilson, was one of their most attractive.

Before we discuss the building of the Tickford Bridge it is worth reviewing the use of cast iron in bridge construction, the growth of British ironmasters, and other early iron bridges.

THE EVOLUTION OF CAST-IRON BRIDGES IN BRITAIN

Iron is an element universally present in various ore combinations in the earth's crust, and was available once the technology of extracting and purifying it had been mastered. Smelting with charcoal at a considerable heat produced pig iron, which could then be heated into a malleable form and, with further heating up to 1,150-1,200 degrees, reduced to a free-running liquid. The liquid iron could then be redirected into pre-formed sand moulds of the desired shape, allowed to cool, and then broken out as the finished article.

In Europe, the mathematical understanding of the behaviour of beams under stress, both under tension and bending, was developed in the late 16th century. In England, the great mathematician and practical experimentalist Robert Hooke (1635-1708) developed the ideas further.

Cast, or 'grey', iron was appreciated as an ideal material for some purposes. It is almost unparalleled in compressive strength: 36-40 tons per square inch (compared with malleable iron at 16-18 tons/in^2), but it is weak both in tension and under bending stresses. Thus, as a bridging material, the semi-circular arch is as near the ideal form as possible.

THE THEORY OF CAST-IRON DESIGN

The properties of cast iron as a constructional material were first developed by Thomas Tredgold in 1824, and by the 1830s William Fairbairn had tested a variety of cast-iron beams and published his empirical formula in 1831.

Since the beginning of the 18th century, the growth in the market of iron products, starting with the invention of iron rails in 1767, the static steam engine, and the locomotive, gave a huge impetus for the growth of ironworks. These large establishments required a lot of capital in order to invest in large-scale cast-iron production, and this, combined with better communications by waterways and canals, resulted in the consolidation of large-scale iron casting in a reduced number of regional centres.

Various experiments had meanwhile taken place in using a combination of cast and wrought iron, utilising the particular advantage that each provided.

Foremost amongst the early British ironmasters who controlled ironworks with the capacity to undertake large castings is the Coalbrookdale Company in Shropshire. Others soon rose up to share in the business, particularly Joshua Walker & Co. in Rotherham; Foster Raistrick & Co. in Stourbridge; the Horesley Ironworks of Tipton, Staffordshire; William Hazledine at Plas Kynaston, near Ruabon; John Wilkinson at Benshall/Brymbo, Denbighshire; Richard Crawshay at Cyfarthfa, Merthyr Tydfil; Benjamin Outram and Jessop at Butterley, Ripley, Derbyshire; and in Scotland, the Carron and Bonawe Ironworks. Many of these companies became involved with the production of, essentially, prefabricated iron bridges.

EARLY IRON BRIDGES IN ENGLAND AND WALES

Early amongst iron bridges are the structurally-related iron aqueducts, primarily serving the rapidly expanding canal systems. Fortunately, three of the earliest still survive. Longdon-on-Tern, near Shrewsbury, of 1796, was the earliest, immediately followed by Chirk and then Pontcysyllte; both for the Shropshire Union Canal. Other, less spectacular, bridges followed, but by 1810 the canal system was up and running and the needs of the canal companies had largely been met. Mention should be made of the Wolverton Iron Trunk, an aqueduct over the River Great Ouse, designed by William Jessop to replace an earlier brick aqueduct which had spectacularly failed, and a temporary system of five locks, up and down. This iron aqueduct, made by Reynolds & Co. of Ketley, was opened for traffic in 1811. Interestingly, the Canal Company's engineer, James Barnes, had already proposed an iron aqueduct as early as 1799, but this had been rejected in favour of the brick solution.

THE COALBROOKDALE IRON BRIDGE

As is widely known, the first iron bridge to be designed and constructed is the Iron Bridge at Coalbrookdale. It was originally proposed as an idea by Shrewsbury architect Thomas Farnolls Pritchard, to the ironmaster John Wilkinson. Wilkinson had two ironworks nearby, one at Bradley in Staffordshire, and another at Willey in Shropshire. His mind was fertile ground, and a comment at the time stated that it was where 'so many improvements are daily making'. He made the first steps towards the implementation of a bridge across the Severn Gorge.

The first discussions regarding constructing a bridge of cast iron were held in Coalbrookdale in 1777 over whether to replace the old river crossing at Buildwas, Shropshire, which was a great inconvenience to the burgeoning industries either side of the River Severn. The first official meeting to discuss the problem of river crossings took place in September 1795, and in October an iron bridge solution was formally proposed. To carry this solution through required Royal assent, and a Bill was drafted and submitted to Parliament on 25 March 1776, 'for making a structure of cast iron, stone, or brick or timber'. Whether the promoters had made a decision to use iron is not recorded, but they may have been keeping their options open in case unforeseen problems should befall the new technology. Eighteen months of indecision and delay were to follow.

The finished bridge differed from Pritchard's plans, perhaps because he had been ill since construction began. It was a semicircular arch of 100-feet 6-inches span, and was supported by abutments on both banks. It rose to 40 feet high at the centre. A total of 378 tons of cold blast iron were used, each rib weighing 5¾ tons. On top it carried a roadway of clay and iron slag on iron plates.

OTHER EARLY BRIDGES

The next two bridges built were small-scale replicas of Coalbrookdale, and in 1791 two further bridges were ordered for the Island of Nevis in the West Indies. Cast iron was the obvious material for use in bridge construction as it

8 *The Coalbrookdale Iron Bridge.*

could be shipped in parts and erected on site. However, neither of the West Indies bridges was built. Back in England in 1794, a cast-iron bridge was ordered by the Marquis of Stafford for his garden, probably Trentham Gardens, near Stoke-on-Trent. This was to be almost as large as Coalbrookdale itself.

From 1795 to 1800, cast iron had become an option to be considered in all cases, and by 1800, optimism for cast-iron bridges had reached its peak, even before the actual completion of the spectacular Pontcysyllte aqueduct near Llangollen. At that time, Coalbrookdale were advertising 'iron bridges of any span or height'.

It was generally believed that the limitation of cast iron was the inability to cast large and very large components without any flaws whatsoever, and the weight of these members that could be handled.

A marvellous opportunity came with the great flood of the River Severn in February 1793. The fact that so many bridges were swept away, and the Ironbridge Gorge Bridge at Coalbrookdale survived intact, did not go unnoticed. Buildwas Bridge over the Severn was replaced by Telford with a bridge spanning 131 feet in 1796; the longest span achieved to date, it used the Schaffenhausen suspension rib. The Coalport Bridge at Preens Eddy was strengthened in 1799, and Pritchard's bridge at Stourport, which was severely damaged by the floods, was also replaced by a single-span arch of iron.

Parallel with the development of iron bridges was that of the suspension bridge. Suspending a deck had, of course, been known from ancient times across the world. A number of large suspension bridges had been built in America, such as Finlay's Jacob's Creek Bridge of 1801, but further developments had taken placed in France and in England, where Captain Samuel Brown introduced his cast-iron chain links. Dated 1819-20, the Union Chain Bridge over the Tweed, linking England and Scotland, near Paxton, Berwick-upon-Tweed, is our earliest example. At almost the same time, Telford's suspension bridge, spanning an astonishing 579 feet over the Menai Strait to Anglesey, was designed in 1818 but not actually finished until 1826. This was closely followed by the 1822 Conwy Bridge, all for the Holyhead Road. Generally, suspension bridges had become discredited, as it became apparent that the suspended deck was far too flexible to carry trains.

WALKER & CO., ROTHERHAM

Walker & Co. of Rotherham, South Yorkshire, who cast the Tickford bridge, were extremely skilled and competent ironworkers. The family began as local farmers and blacksmiths. Samuel Walker, previously a teacher, founded a smithy business in 1741 at Grenoside, Eccleshall, near Sheffield, with his brothers, Aaron and Jonathan. In 1746 the brothers moved the business to Masbrough, near Rotherham, where John Crawshaw became a partner, and where they built a new casting house conveniently close beside the River Don. The factory expanded in 1753-4, and again in 1757-9, by taking on leases of the Holmes Estate. A huge government order for armaments, initiated by the Prime Minister Charles Watson-Wentworth, the second Marquis of Rockingham (incidentally a local landowner), led to their producing an immense quantity of cannons of large calibre, and the appropriate shot. Samuel Walker died in 1782, and his four sons followed him as equal partners.

Joshua Walker borrowed money from the Marquis of Rockingham and bought out Crawshaw. The remaining partners then built a blast furnace on the Earl of Effingham's estate at The Holmes. Samuel Walker II died in 1782, and the Earl sold his estate, Holmes Hall, to the Walkers, who were trading as Joshua Walker & Co. Holmes Iron Works from 1792.

TOM PAINE AND HIS INTEREST IN BRIDGE DESIGN

Following the end of the American War of Independence, engineering progress was being made in the former colony. Thomas [Tom] Paine (1737-1809), the great political philosopher and champion of human rights was, amongst everything else, an engineering philosopher as well as a practical genius. Although English by birth, he had emigrated to America in 1774 to support American independence from Britain. He was well acquainted with the development of bridge design represented by the Coalbrookdale arch, but sought to improve on its current methodology of using large castings, which he deemed to be too cumbersome to handle economically.

Tom Paine returned to England, 'looking for practical iron men', and so discovered Walkers of Rotherham, a well capitalised company. He had heard that the Joshua Walker & Co. Holmes Iron Works were valued at £200,000, and had taken out his own patent the same year for the construction of ribbed iron bridges using small segments as voussoirs to build up the spans.

In 1788, Walkers were planning a bridge across the Don in Yorkshire. Paine persuaded them to make an experimental arch of cast iron in their works, which was duly erected and tested. Although Paine hoped it would be the prototype for a bridge over the Thames, it seems that the design was eventually used for the bridge over the River Don. His personal fame and the novelty of his design system led to a stream of distinguished visitors. The experimental bridge had four ribs, spanned 90 feet, and carried six tons.

Following this success, another bridge was made, shipped to London for public exhibition, and was erected in the grounds of a public house in Paddington, the *Yorkshire Stingo*, in the summer of 1790. Despite all this publicity, the bridge was dismantled, returned to Yorkshire, and sold as scrap!

Walkers by 1805 had built up a great reputation for producing new cast-iron bridges, but at the end of the war in Europe in 1815 their trade of heavy armaments was less in demand. The firm changed its focus to other things, amongst which were bridges. A visitor to Walkers' Foundry at Rotherham, back in 1801, concluded that 'cast iron bridges are put up at a fifth part of the cost, in one tenth the amount of time, and are more durable'.

Altogether, from 1793 to 1816, Walkers produced no less than a dozen significant cast-iron bridges, and probably a number of smaller ones of which records no longer survive. Of these, by far the most famous was the great iron bridge to cross the River Wear at Sunderland.

THE SUNDERLAND BRIDGE

The need for a bridge over the River Wear at Sunderland was an important economic requirement for the expanding local industries on both banks of the river, and the two local members of Parliament, Rowland Burdon IV and Ralph Milbanke, had promised to investigate the possibilities in their election speeches.

Rowland Burdon IV (1756-1836), a banker, and member of parliament for Durham, was part of a landed and mercantile family from Castle Eden, and claimed he had studied architecture under (Sir) John Soane. As a local landowner he was very much concerned with the development of the port of Sunderland as an outlet for locally manufactured goods. He had already taken an interest in engineering and had assembled a number of alternative bridge designs in stone, wood and iron.

The specification for the Sunderland Bridge outlined a number of demanding new problems. Firstly, the bridge had to be 230-feet or more span, it had to have a single arch, and had to be tall enough to permit tall-masted ships to pass beneath. In 1792, Burdon submitted a Bill requesting Parliament to allow a new bridge to be built. The Act received Royal Assent in June of that year. Of the alternative construction materials considered, stone, at the estimated cost of £70,000, proved to be too expensive, and doubts were expressed about the permanence of wood.

Burdon disapproved of the methodology behind the Coalbrookdale Bridge. He had promoted his method using cast-iron box voussoirs, assembled as stone – he believed that large and heavy iron castings were difficult and expensive to handle. Burdon had already taken out a patent on a modified version of the Coalbrookdale design, and had made contact with the American émigré, Thomas Paine, who had been thinking along the same lines. With the design skills he had acquired, Burdon was probably the lead designer behind the new Sunderland Bridge Project. He engaged, or at least teamed up with, a local

9   *The 1793 iron bridge over the Wear at Sunderland, before Stephenson's remodelling.*

Sunderland engineer/architect, Thomas Wilson, who later took out his own patent. Probably through Paine's influence, they approached one of the leading iron foundries, Walkers of Rotherham, who, in 1792, had built a new casting house. That year, after Samuel II died, the firm became Joshua Walker & Co.

The new Sunderland Bridge, 12 feet wide, spanned 236 feet over the Wear with a segmental arch of 444-foot diameter and reached 100 feet. It consisted of six arch rings, assembled from 105 small components. Construction began in 1793, but was not finished until 1796, when on 9 August the bridge was formally opened by Prince William of Gloucester at a well-attended Masonic ceremony. As the largest single-span iron bridge in the world at the time, it rapidly became a famous site, pictured on lustrewares, on glassware from Southwick, and in many etchings and engravings. It subsequently seemed that insufficient provision had been made for expansion, resulting in some cracking of components and the dropping away of the spacer bars; George Stephenson was called in over 1858-9 to remedy the situation. Stephenson retained the six original ribs but replaced much else and added the inscription *Nil Desperandum, Auspice Deo*, perhaps indicating a slight degree of apprehension on his own part. The demolition of this bridge, in as late as 1929, must go down in history as one of the greatest losses of an industrial monument of world class.

John Nash claimed, falsely, to have designed the Sunderland Bridge. In 1795, however, he did design a bridge for Sir Edward Winnington to cross the River Teme at Stanford Court, Worcestershire. The bridge collapsed soon after completion, however. The Coalbrookdale Company disclaimed any involvement with this, but they did make a second bridge for Sir Winnington at Stanford, on Nash's patent of 1797. This bridge survived until it was replaced in ferro-concrete 1911.

At this time, Joshua Walker & Co. were supremely confident in their own right.

Paine, it seems, always kept his sights high. Before his recall to America in 1802 by his old friend President Thomas Jefferson, he may have been consulted on the design of the 181-foot span over the Thames at Staines, Middlesex; a bridge that was begun in 1802. Seven years later, in 1809, after his return to America, Tom Paine died aged 65, sad, lonely, and in penury.

It is unlikely that Walkers' other smaller bridges would have engaged his genius. Bridges such as Wilson's design of the bridge crossing the Rio Cobre in Spanish Town, then the capital of the British colony of Jamaica, and manufactured by Walker & Co., was cast in 1800, shipped to the West Indies in 1801, and erected on site during 1801-2. The date 1801 is cast on the side. As a main road bridge, it was superseded in October 1931 by the Stubbs Bridge a few yards further down the river. Remarkably, it still survives. Thomas Wilson also produced the design of the delicate little bridge at Stratfield Saye which, like the Spanish Town bridge, is also dated 1801 on the side (*see* Fig. 11). The family of George Pitt, Lord Rivers, who commissioned this bridge, owned collieries in County Durham, which therefore might account for its unexpected appearance in North Hampshire.

Bridges could be provided for any purpose. Coalbrookdale made a bridge, designed by John Dodson, to carry the Much Wenlock to Shrewsbury Road over the Cound Brook, of 40-foot span, but it was replaced in 1918. Another iron bridge over the Cound Brook at Cound Arbour nearby still survives bearing the date 1797. Manufacturers often took such opportunities to advertise, as did Plas Kynaston on the Craigellachie Bridge and the Brymbo Ironworks on the Brynderwyn Bridge at Abermiwl, Powys.

10 *The Spanish
Town Bridge,
Jamaica.*

11 *Stratfield Saye Bridge of 1802. Designed by Thomas Wilson and built by Walkers.*

PROBLEMS

Cast-iron bridges were not all an unmitigated success. Thomas Wilson's bridge of 1803, made by Walkers, spanning 180 feet over the Thames at Staines, sagged when the centreing was removed. At Yarm in Teesside, the bridge of 1803-5, of which the Mayor said at the opening 'may the Almighty protect this undertaking', collapsed into the river 'with an enormous crash' at midnight on 12 January 1806 after only three years of life. Ironically, Bishop Skirlaw's bridge of 1270, which the Yarm Bridge was designed to replace, still stands to this day. Some of the failures need not be put down to the inadequacy of iron as a constructional material, or to any incompetence in the design; there were frequent failures of the abutments, such as that which happened at Yarm and at Staines, which at that time were less easily calculable.

THE TOWN BRIDGE, BOSTON

12 (Above left) Manufacturer's plate by Plas Kynaston Ironworks on the Craigellachie Bridge.

13 (Below Left) The Brymbo Ironworks' manufacturer's plate for the Brynderwyn Bridge over the River Severn, Powys.

Immediately prior to the commissioning of the Tickford Bridge, Walkers were engaged in replacing the dilapidated timber bridge across the River Wensum at Boston, erected in 1742 but which was then in a perilous condition.

The new bridge was designed by John Rennie, who had been carrying out work on the course of the River Witham from Boston to Lincoln since 1803 and was already well known to the town authorities. The new bridge, made by Walkers of Rotherham, was no doubt shipped along the Don to the Humber, and carried by sea to the Witham.

A pen and watercolour drawing of July 1806 by W. Brand in Boston Borough Archives shows the east abutment in the south-west angle. The foundation stone was laid on 2 August 1806 by the Mayor. The abutments consisted of 26 courses of stone set on 26 close-spaced piles, with further piles under the terminal piers.

The new bridge, illustrated in a litho print, also in Boston Borough archives, shows a suspended lower string arcade and gothic arches in the spandrels. Above this is an outsetting modillion cornice carrying a balustraded handrail with dog rails, and at the centre there are pyramidal lamp standards each side, each carrying a circular badge with the town's coat of arms, recalling the Tickford Bridge.

Following a series of accidents caused by boats colliding with it, the bridge had to be replaced in 1913 by a new bridge designed by John Webster. This has a cast-iron parapet. Walkers' cast-iron bridge was demolished as soon as the first arch of the new bridge was in place, and a photograph (Wright, 1994) shows that the old bridge collapsed into the river during demolition, with the ship *Privateer* in front.

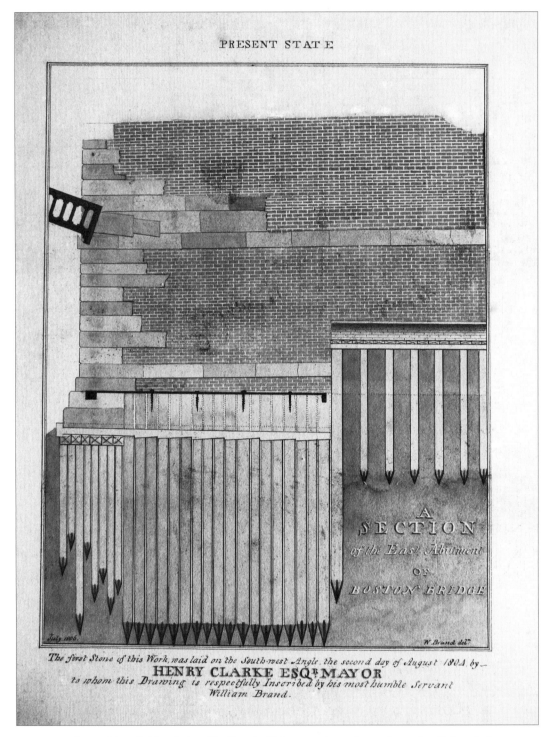

PRESENT STATE

A
SECTION
of the East Abutment
OF
BOSTON BRIDGE

July 1806.

W. Brand delt.

The first Stone of this Work, was laid on the South-west Angle, the second day of August 1804 by
HENRY CLARKE ESQ: MAYOR
*to whom this Drawing is respectfully Inscribed by his most humble Servant
William Brand.*

14 *Boston Town Bridge, designed by Rennie. This watercolour of 1806 shows the pile foundations.*

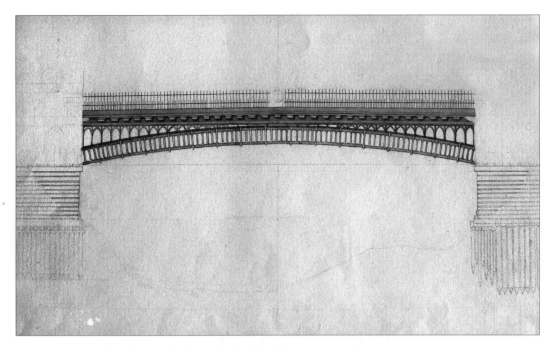

15   *A lithograph of the Boston Town Bridge, 1806, by W. Brand.*

The interesting fact is that the Town Bridge was designed according to the Burdon-Paine principles, with an assemblage of small castings, unlike Wilson's Tickford Bridge, designed some two years later. A firm of Walkers' experience are unlikely simply to have accepted the engineer's design without question, and some other factor may have entered the decision-making. Perhaps it may indicate that Walkers had some reservations about the Burdon-Paine method, or perhaps large castings were preferred for smaller spans (the Boston Town Bridge spanned 83 feet; the Tickford Bridge spanned 56 feet), and where speed of erection was an important factor. It cannot be claimed that it was easier to ship large elements to Newport Pagnell.

Thomas Wilson proposed a new London Bridge at Southwark in 1813. It was along the lines of the Sunderland Bridge, with one arch of 240-foot span and two of 220 feet. Telford had produced two alternative schemes, one for a single arch, as was Wilsons, and another for a five-arch bridge. Wilson then proposed another alternative, this time with the span reduced. Not to be outdone, Telford produced his own scheme for a single arch of 600 feet based on a segment of a circle 1,450 feet in diameter.

Walkers, who had always been comfortable with their contracts and their finances, gradually seem to have lost their earlier pioneering spirit, and the design initiative passed to other firms, including their original rivals, the Coalbrookdale Company. To what extent the enormous outstanding debt owed for 10 years to Walkers for their work on the Southwark Bridge was to blame is not known, but their last furnace closed down in 1823, and by 1830 they had ceased trading. This is somewhat surprising since by the 1830s and 1840s the demand for bridges leapt enormously due to the expansion of the railways.

For a list of surviving cast-iron bridges in the country, earlier than the Tickford Bridge, which is the only one to carry all types of modern traffic, *see* Appendix Two.

7

The Construction of the Tickford Bridge

O nce the North Bridge was open and income from the tolls flowed into their account, the attention of the Trustees turned to the Tickford Bridge. At a meeting on 6 February 1810 the Trustees unanimously resolved that the old stone bridge should be replaced with an iron bridge.

One of the Trustees, the Rev. Richard Cautley of Moulsoe, who had visited Sunderland to discuss the construction of iron bridges, reported back to the Trustees who thanked him for procuring information respecting the plans and construction of iron bridges and the comparative expense and convenience of stone and iron bridges.

At a meeting on 6 February 1810 the Trustees unanimously resolved:

That an Iron Bridge be erected in the room of the present Tickford Bridge, and that the Rev. Richard Cautley be requested to correspond with Mr Wilson on the subject of the construction thereof, and that he do treat for the erection of the bridge and the execution of the work.

In 1802, Thomas Wilson and Rowland Burdon, Member of Parliament for Durham, had taken out a patent on a modified version of the Wearmouth Bridge. The Tickford Bridge was largely based on that design. Wilson chose Messrs Walkers of Rotherham, the leading ironmasters in the country, to produce the Tickford Bridge. Walkers had produced the Sunderland Bridge and been involved with other bridges that he had designed.

The Trustees chose Henry Provis (1760-1830) as resident engineer. Formerly of Paddington he had come to the area as Senior Site Supervisor for the construction of Tyringham House, working under the architect Sir John Soane. He then became district engineer for the Grand Junction Canal Company, now known as the Grand Union Canal. He took up residence at

16 (Above) Bridge House, Sherington, home of Henry Provis from 1815-30.

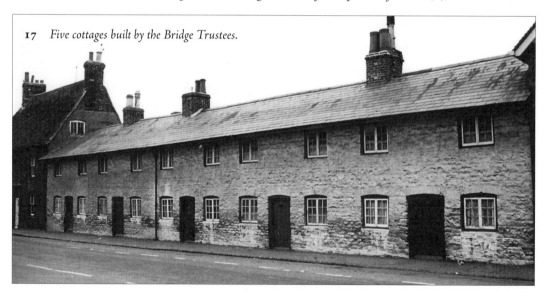

17 Five cottages built by the Bridge Trustees.

Bridge House Sherington (*see* Fig. 16), a pleasant Regency-style house before its many extensions, beside the Toll House, where he continued to live with his family until his death in 1830. Provis was responsible for the design and building of the Toll House and also for the row of cottages just south of Tickford Bridge (*see* Fig. 17). From 1810-11 he undertook the supervision of the preparatory work and abutments for the Tickford Iron Bridge. He was eventually appointed County Surveyor for North Buckinghamshire in 1819, and for the whole county in 1822; a post which he held up to his death at the age of 70 on 23 August 1830. Provis designed and built Sherington and Olney bridges, amongst others in the county. His career had included working on models for the Bank of England for Sir John Soane, and at Tyringham.

For the actual assembly of the iron work of Tickford Bridge, Walkers sent William Yates, who had the necessary experience having acted as foreman for the erection of the Sunderland Bridge. It is a compliment to Yates' proven abilities that in 1816 John Rennie was to trust to his competent hands the designing of the detail of the Southwark Iron Bridge. At 200 feet it was to be the longest in Britain at that date.

The bridge was ordered soon after the meeting in February, and the ground work and foundations for the abutments were commenced soon after this. The bridge was built on the upstream side and, just to the south of the old stone bridge, a new course for the river was cut on the south side of the old one. The meadow on the west side of the bridge was put up for auction in May 1810, when it was described as bounded 'on the south by the River Lovat as the same is now excavated and formed to pass under an arch of Iron shortly intended to be erected'.

On 16 June 1810, the *Northampton Mercury* reported that the first stone of the abutments for the Tickford Bridge had been laid on the previous Saturday by Henry Provis.

No detailed accounts of the dates of the construction of the bridge survive. The earliest illustration (frontispiece) and description of the bridge is by John Hassel, writing in 1819, as follows:

> The new bridge over the Lovat, usually called Tickford Bridge, consists of one single arch of cast iron, 60 feet in the span; the abutments are of the same kind of stone as the North Bridge, and are sunk down to the solid rock, at the depth of 18 feet below. In digging the foundations of these bridges a quantity of oak timber was found buried at a considerable depth, which evidently appeared to have been the remains of wooden bridges that had stood on the same spots previous to the erection of the old stone bridges that were lately pulled down.

A VIEW OF NEWPORT PAGNEL BRIDGE.

Dedicated to I. Knibb Esq.

18   *The Tickford Iron Bridge by R. Jefferson, 1820.*

Hassel stated that both the town's new bridges 'were built by Mr Provis of Paddington, an engineer of celebrity, from his own designs; they are specimens of durability and pure taste, and highly ornamental to the entrances of the town either way'. Hassel's statement was not quite correct as only the abutments of Tickford Bridge were designed by Provis. Hassel's drawing of the bridge makes it appear as a slightly pointed arch and shows quite different central lamp standards from those in the print, from a drawing by R. Jefferson, dated May 1820.

Jefferson was possibly a member of the family of fellmongers, who had a house and yard on the Tickford side of the bridge. The picture he drew was 'Dedicated to I Knibb Esq, by his most obedient servant R Jefferson'. Knibb may have been James Knibb, a local stonemason from Stoke Goldington, who could have worked on the bridge.

The length of time taken by Walkers to cast the bridge is uncertain, but a likely timetable is that it was completed by mid-June. Assuming this, the bridge parts would have been transported to Newport Pagnell by early July. The assembly of the arch would probably have taken no more than two weeks. Two weeks does not sound a significant length of time, but the arch of the Wearmouth Bridge, which had a span of 236 feet, was assembled in 16 days. Once the arch was in place, the roadway was constructed over it and the flank walls at either end erected.

We can be sure that the work was completed and the bridge in a safe state for traffic to cross it by 29 September 1810, when William Wheatley, the newly appointed Collector of the Tolls, commenced his duties on the Tickford Bridge from a new Toll House (*see* Fig. 19).

John Crament, who had worked on the North Bridge, acted as Clerk of the Works during the erection of the Tickford Bridge. He was assisted in the final assembly by William Yates, the site engineer sent by Walkers to supervise the assembly of the bridge sections, which were all numbered, using iron dowels and keys. No bolts at all were used. Yates was in Newport Pagnell and was paid £5 on 21 July 1810, which must have been when he was advising on the assembly of the bridge. He received two further payments: £35 in January 1811 and £30 11s. 9d., the 'final balance of his bill', in September 1811.

The Trustees' accounts record payments to Walkers and other contractors, which give us the cost of the bridge and its transport. However, as the payments

19 *John Holman Mitchell with his men outside the Tickford Bridge Toll House.*

were deferred until the Trustees had an income from the tolls, they provide no precise evidence of the actual dates when the work took place.

Walkers were paid for their work in three instalments: £1,000 in April 1811; £540 18s. 0d. in November 1812; and a final payment of £300 5s. in February 1814. The total cost, including the carriage from Rotherham to the coast and by sea to London, was £1,840 3s. From London the castings of the bridge were transported by canal to Great Linford wharf by Messrs Sargent & Co. at a cost of £108 13s. 6d., paid in August 1811. A payment of £52 14s. 8d. to the Grand Junction Canal Company in May 1812 must be connected to the cost of transport. For the final part of the journey to Newport Pagnell they were carried by cart, for which a Mr Scrivener was paid £35 6d. in October 1811.

Once both bridges were opened to everyday traffic the accounts mainly record the income from the tolls, which from April 1811 to April 1812 were £1,121 for the North Bridge, where the gate keeper was paid one guinea a week, and £266 for the Tickford Bridge, where the Gate keeper received only 10s. 6d. a week.

In February 1812, William Provis' bill for £203 7s. 3d. was received and considered to be exorbitant. The Trustees felt he was not entitled to more than £105 for his professional assistance, £21 for expenses, and £12 2s. 7d. for payments made for stamps, wharfage, barrow-lime, etc., totalling £138 2s. 7d. In December the Trustees resolved that the sum offered to Provis was sufficient compensation for his services, but this matter was not resolved for some time.

Now that the bridges were built, the main items dealt with by the treasurer were paying outstanding accounts, collecting money from debtors and the day-to-day maintenance of the bridges and the approach roads to them.

Although the Tickford Bridge was completed, a considerable amount of work was required on the approaches to it. In April 1811, John Walker, the surveyor, was ordered to obtain earth and other materials for making, widening, altering or improving the Tickford Bridge and its approaches. The materials were to come from Castle Meadow and notice was to be given to the owner, Philip Hoddle Ward, that John Crament was to take away such part of Castle Meadow near the river for the purpose of getting materials for the embankment, which was necessary on both sides to take account of the arch of the bridge. Evidence of the quarrying can still be seen close to the river in Castle Meadow. The raising of the road, particularly in St John Street, caused considerable inconvenience to householders as their homes and businesses were now below the level of the road (see p.54).

It was also considered necessary to remove two old houses in Tickford Street opposite the Toll House, one belonging to Mr Jefferson and the other to the Town Land Feoffees.

There are no records of the number of men employed during the construction of the bridges or the amount they were paid. Only John Crament appears in the accounts. It is clear that he was a trusted employee and a very busy man. From November 1809 he was the gate keeper for the North Bridge but still continued as the Clerk of Works for both bridges, responsible for paying the workers, purchasing some materials and items needed for the work, and for collecting debts. He received regular payments from the Trustees to cover the wages and expenses, and met the Treasurer every Monday morning to give him the income from the tolls and any outstanding accounts that he had collected.

In August 1811 he was paid almost £100 for his wages up to 1 January 1811. Later, in April, the Trustees agreed to keep him on in the same two positions until midsummer. In January 1812 he was paid £54 12s. for one year's work at one guinea a week as gate keeper on the North Bridge. In addition to this he received an extra 5s. for fuel, and 10s. 6d. a week as surveyor of the bridges.

Two months later Crament ceased to be the gate keeper as the Trustees had decided to put the tolls arising from the North Bridge and Tickford Bridge out to tender. The successful bidder was Thomas Yeandle of Kettering, who was granted a lease for one year from 6 April at the rent of £1,610. He was allowed to pay in monthly installments, but was to provide security to confirm that he could pay. With this income the Trustees were now able to pay Mansell Dawkin Mansel and Charlotte Beaty for the land purchased from them for the construction of the North Bridges. John Crament measured the land for which the Trustees paid £200 per acre compensation.

After this, Crament's work was completed and he is not mentioned again in the Accounts or Minute Books after June 1812.

From quite early times Newport had been an important stopping place for travellers from London to the East Midlands and the north of England. The reconstruction of the bridges greatly improved transport through the town, improving the lot of the local inn and hostelry owners and the associated trades.

The bridges, now completed, allowed the Trustees to look forward to a busy and prosperous future. The income from the tolls allowed them to repay all of the money to the subscribers by 1826, after which the collection of tolls was stopped.

The last subscribers to be repaid were the Rev. Thomas Palmer Bull: £750, and Mr William Andrews of Lathbury: £100.

Constructional Details of Tickford Bridge

The bridge comprises six segmental arch rings, each of identical form, with plate abutments at each end. In elevation, it has a lower string course of decorative rings linked by moulded collars, made in 11 sections, apparently joined at the shackles for the cross spacers. Each section is numbered with elegant figures at the ends, close to the casting sprue scar (*see* Fig. 20). On this are set the spandrels; which consist of two castings of diminishing rings, one of three large rings and one of five smaller rings with a 'dagger' at the end. It is not clear how these are secured to the lower arch rings, but the two ring panels were joined by a tongue and groove vertical joint. Above the spandrels is the fascia, consisting of five moulded panels, the centre one (*see* Fig. 21) carrying the date '1810' on each side. Above this is set the balustrade, consisting of five sections of bold balusters with intermediate dog rails, with an upper string of 'X' figures cast as one with the balustrade, all elements of identical cross section. These sections are joined at decorative openwork panels. To finish, the capping handrail is made in five sections, mounted on top of the upper rail of the 'X' frieze, and at the centre carrying the decorative lamp stanchions which may be a later addition to the bridge when gas was brought through, as they do not appear on the Hassel and Jefferson illustrations of 1819-20 (*see* cover and Fig. 1). The rail is set and run in with lead into the limestone piers, which are continued as ashlar retaining walls scrolled out to terminal piers. These carried elegant iron stanchions on four splayed feet for oil lamps. The two on the southern end of the bridge still survive (but without the inserted lamps), but the two at the north end have long since disappeared. The stone for the abutments was quarried at Sallage Close, Newport Pagnell. It consists of faced ashlar on the outer side, set over point-dressed squared rubble below the parapet level.

The main arch rings are joined horizontally by a series of 10 heavy cast-iron shackles or spacers consisting of two upper round bars, and two lower bars, linked midway between each arch (*see* Fig. 22).

It is not exactly clear how the bridge was cast and assembled. The abutment plates (*see* Fig. 23) are in three sections, but it seems greatly improbable that two arches were cast with their abutment plates as one single casting, as their transportation, if this was so, would seem seriously impracticable. Yet it is difficult to see how else they were put together. Clearly the lower string of rings

20 (Above) Assembly numbers on the bottom string of the Tickford Bridge.

21 (Right) The fascia showing the date of construction and the lamp standards, Tickford Bridge.

22 (Above) The east face of Tickford Bridge showing the cross shackles.

23 (Right) Tickford Bridge abutment plates.

24 *Stratfield Saye Bridge, showing assembly numbers on the handrail stanchions.*

was assembled on site as each section was numbered (*see* Fig. 20) at each end, 1–10 from the north bank, and the fascia was assembled from five individual sections, as was the handrail. As mentioned earlier, the numbering of parts for assembly was also observed on the handrail stanchions of the Stratfield Saye Bridge (*see* Fig. 24), even to using what appear to be the same irons to imprint the casting sand. The road deck consisted of a number of flanged bowed plates which were bolted together, upon which the road formation was built up. In the condition survey made by P.J. Peters, it was observed that the sections did not all meet precisely, and in the case of the spandrels, the upper joint was packed out with scrap iron and filled with weak red lead putty.

25   *The Sydney Gardens Bridge, Bath, showing the ring spandrels of 1800.*

26   *Cross-braced spandrels at Llandinam Bridge.*

27   *The decorative bottom string of Brynderwyn Bridge, inscribed with the date of construction: 1852.*

The idea of filling the open spandrels with diminishing rings as bracings seems rather illogical and probably originated with the cylindrical piercings used to relieve the pressure on the abutments of early stone bridges, such as William Edwards' famous third attempt to bridge the wild River Taff at Pontypridd in 1755. Circular rings of iron are used in the spandrels at Ironbridge and became a stock in trade of the industry, as at Sydney Gardens Bridge, Bath (*see* Fig. 25), and even appearing on the Bridgwater Bridge as late as 1883. Elsewhere they were gradually being replaced from 1828 onwards with lattice bracing, as at Llandinam, Powys, 1843 (*see* Fig. 26), and even enhanced at times with a decorative lower string as at the Waterloo Bridge at Betws-y-Coed, and the Brynderwyn Bridge over the River Severn at Abermiwl, Powys (*see* Fig. 27).

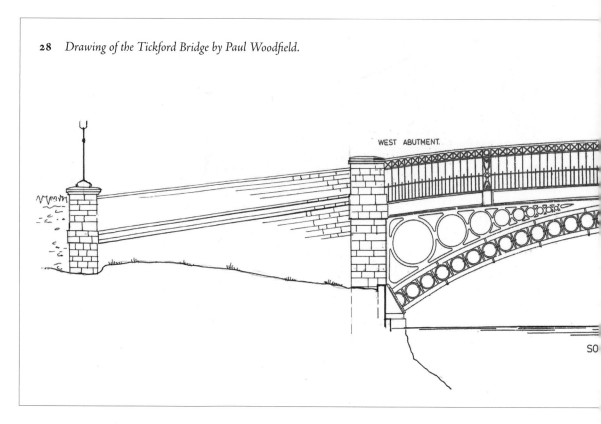

28 *Drawing of the Tickford Bridge by Paul Woodfield.*

The Tickford Bridge, although it superficially looks to be in its original state, has suffered some indignities. The western face has had a large pipe suspended from plates clasping the bottom of the handrail stanchions, and another service pipe is more inconspicuously suspended beneath the centre. The central lamp standard on the same side has been carefully plated and bolted at its junction with the handrail where it had at some time been fractured, and a cross bar for a ladder has been added. When the central lights were connected to the town's gas supply, the oil lamps on the terminal piers were probably seen as redundant. The abutments show slight signs of a continuation of leaning inwards, as is frequently the case with abutments, but this does not seem to be enough to cause damage to the castings.

As to detail, the surviving schedule of parts shipped by Walkers for the Spanish Town Bridge will give some idea of the sort of package which would have arrived by canal at Linford Wharf, for onward carriage to Newport Pagnell. The Spanish Town Bridge is of course a rather larger span at 82 feet, compared with Newport's 58 feet.

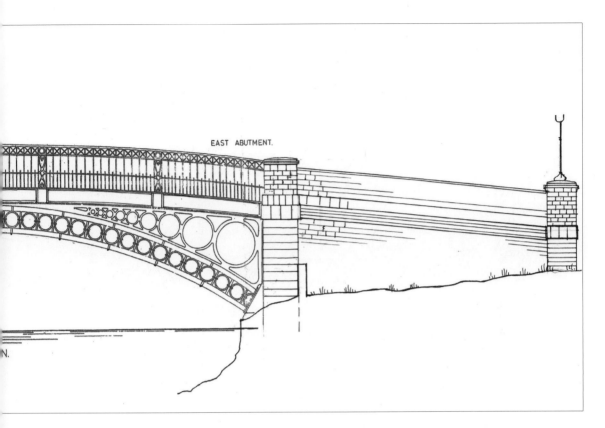

EAST ABUTMENT.

COMPONENTS OF THE SPANISH TOWN BRIDGE

Skewback shoes or plates	8
Voussoir units	80
Central unit	4
Transverse tubular connectors	120
Spandrel elements 3 large circles	8
Compressed circles	8
Cornice elements	4 + 10 longer ones
Balustrade stanchions and finials	14
Fascia elements	16
Flanges deck plates	41
Baluster rails standard	16
Balusters standard	304
Total weight of the ironwork:	**86.1 tons**

An assembly diagram of this and the comparative assembly of the very similar bridge in Stratfield Saye is shown in Fig. 29.

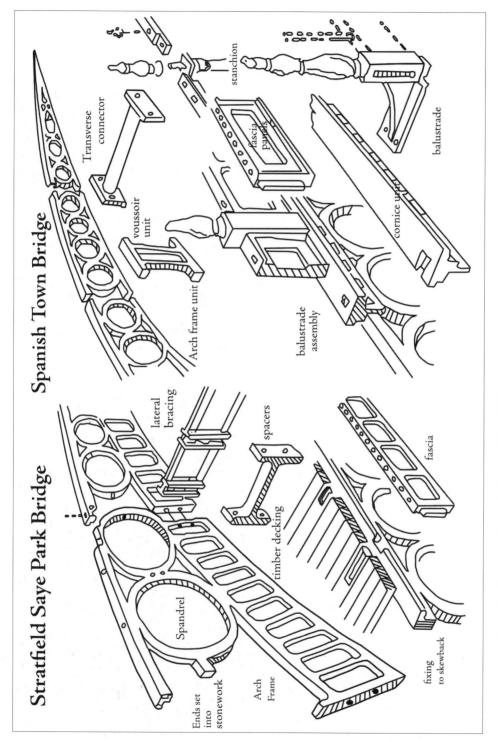

Spanish Town Bridge

Transverse connector

voussoir unit

Arch frame unit

stanchion

fascia panels

balustrade

cornice unit

balustrade assembly

Stratfield Saye Park Bridge

lateral bracing

spacers

fascia

Spandrel

timber decking

Ends set into stonework

Arch Frame

fixing to skewback

29   *Assembly diagrams of Spanish Town and Stratfield Saye bridges, after a drawing by Kingston University, Jamaica.*

8

The Nineteenth Century

THE HEYDAY OF THE COACHING TRADE

With the bridges now open for traffic, the Trustees were responsible for an ongoing programme of maintenance and repair of the bridges and repair and resurfacing of the roadways. They also sought to improve the roadways in the town. It was in their interest to keep traffic flowing with as few impediments as possible.

In addition to improving the road surfaces and also those of the footpaths through the town, they sought, as most planners would, to widen the roads, even if this meant purchasing and demolishing property along the route.

A house in the North End was purchased for this purpose in 1816. The deed of conveyance recorded that 'the same is marked out and intended to be part of the Public Highway or approach to the North Bridge'.

In June 1817 the Trustees considered an offer from Mrs Hillyer, the owner of the *Ram Inn*, for the sale of a small piece of ground at the Ram Corner, opposite the Church in the High Street. Mrs Hillyer had recently suffered bereavement through the death of her husband. This would have neatly rounded off the corner, improving a tight spot on the way through the town. However, her offer was not accepted and improvement of the corner was not carried out until 1888 when the land was purchased to allow the proposed Newport Pagnell to Olney tramway lines to be laid.

In 1825 the Trustees attempted to buy a house at Cannon Corner, then in the occupation of Widow Leverett, to enable them to improve the 'Avenues and Approaches' to the Bridges. However, she would not sell, and the Minute Books record that 'as doubts exist as to the Powers of the Trustees to compel a sale, Counsels Opinion should be taken'. Obviously the advice was that they did not have the power of compulsory purchase and the sale could not proceed.

The Trustees did, however, continue to carry out the alterations, and amendments commenced on Saint John Street down to Tickford Bridge which were to be completed as soon as convenient. Needless to say, some inhabitants were not happy that the pavements were raised above the floor level of their houses and the Committee was instructed to 'treat with those persons who may conceive themselves to have suffered damage as a result of the alterations'. There is no mention of compensation, and in fact the inhabitants of houses on the east side of St John Street, including the customers of the *Admiral Hood* public house, had to go down steps into their properties, until they were demolished almost 150 years later in the 1950s.

Whilst the townspeople complained, travellers passing through the town were pleased with the improvements.

An interesting account of the traffic on the road in 1820 was by Thomas Dunning, who as a child of seven was brought to Newport Pagnell. Later in life he wrote his reminiscences which include the following:

> Newport is fifty miles from London on the great road from London to Chester and Holyhead, and a great number of stage-coaches, gentleman's carriages, four and six-horse luggage wagons, fly vans, etc., including the Chester and Holyhead mail-coach passed through Newport daily to and from London, changing horses at the hotels and inns.

> Newport in former times was of dangerous approach, by reason of the overflowing of the Ouse. It stands between the Ouse and the Lovat near their junction and, although there are fine bridges over both rivers, it still suffers much from floods. During floods, several streets are rendered impassable to pedestrians, the water at full flood rising as high as the bedroom windows of the cottages, and as it lowers carts are sent round containing provisions for the imprisoned inhabitants, who take them in from their second storey windows.

> I remember that on several occasions the Chester mail was delayed several hours, not venturing to cross the rapid stream at the end of the bridge.

The heavy traffic meant that repairs to the road surfaces, and also to the fencing and walls at the side of the road on the approaches to the bridges, were regularly required. The Trustees granted a contract to a Benjamin Taylor for repair of the highways at the end of the bridges at the rate of £30 per annum. Taylor proposed an iron palisade fence to be erected at the north end of Tickford Bridge on the side next to Price's blacksmith's shop, after a similar pattern to the other side (*see* Fig. 30) and not exceeding that length. These fences replaced

30   *The Tickford Bridge, 1858.*

earlier wooden ones. The job was finished off neatly with kerb stones placed adjoining the footpath on the Tickford Bridge.

The Trustees occasionally dealt with claims by coach owners whose vehicles were damaged by projecting signs or parts of buildings and vice versa for people whose property was damaged by passing coaches and wagons. In 1821 the Bridge Surveyor was directed to 'lay information against George Labrum, of Newport Pagnell Wharf, for damage done by his Waggon to the Lamp Iron at the North Bridge'.

Following this, the Committee of Management arranged for a printed notice to be placed on each of the bridges 'to caution Persons against damaging or defacing the Walls, Lamp Posts, or Bridges'.

The town now flourished with an increase in coach traffic and the resultant number of visitors passing through. *Pigot's Directory* of 1823-4 quoted the population as just over 3,000. The Post Office was at the *Swan*, the main coaching inn which was run by Ann Higgins, Post Mistress. The three principal inns, the *Swan*, the *Saracen's Head* and *The George*, stood in a row on the south side of the High Street, with large yards at the rear running down to St John Street and the Tickford Bridge. Many coaches broke their journeys to Holyhead, Liverpool, Manchester, Sheffield and Leeds by stopping in Newport Pagnell. An east-west coach service also ran between Cambridge and Oxford.

Within 10 years the coach trade had increased, with over 30 coaches a day breaking their journeys in the town.

From the *Swan* the Chester mail coach departed at 12 a.m. to London and another returned at about 2 a.m.

The coaching inns also flourished: the *Swan*, run by Ann Higgins from 1801-20, followed by Thomas Brown, from 1821-44; the *Saracen's Head*, run by the Clarke family from 1803-22, then Luke Newbury from 1823-7; and *The George*, run by Luke Newbury from 1813-22, after which he went to the *Saracen's Head*. There were also at least 20 taverns and public houses in the town, many of which had stabling in their yards where horses were kept for coaches that needed to change them. The large number of horses stabled ensured plenty of work for the five blacksmiths and farriers in the town.

You could travel to most parts of the country from Newport Pagnell. Coaches left the town for Chester, Derby, Holyhead, Leeds, Leicester, London, Liverpool, Manchester, Northampton, Sheffield and many other places en-route.

The town's economy was largely based on income from the coaching trade and the lace trade which employed many local women. As well as coaches, the roads were busy with wagons and carts owned by carriers who plied their trade to and from local villages and towns, Newport Pagnell and London. The services to London were impressive. Pickford's caravan ran everyday, to the *Bell Inn*, Wood Street, Cheapside; Atterbury's waggon ran Monday and Thursday to the *Windmill*, St Johns Street; whilst Holt, Marshall and Cole's caravan went to the *Axe Inn*, Aldermanbury, on Wednesday and Saturday.

The continuous pounding of the horse's hooves and the wheels of carts and carriages resulted in the roads being continually in need of repair. In October 1825 the approach to the North Bridge was re-paved with chopped local stone to the end of the wing wall, and the paving of the Tickford Bridge was also repaired.

It is interesting to note that this is the first time that the Trustees referred to Tickford Bridge as the Iron Bridge. This name, not used again in the Minute Books until 1865, became the name by which the bridge was known to all local people.

By 1826 the income from the tolls had repaid many of those that loaned money in the early years. Tolls were still charged, but on 4 August that year it was decided that the Toll Gates on Tickford Bridge were to be taken down and removed at midday on 6 November.

The flood waters in the River Ouse took their toll on the north (upstream) abutment of the principal arch of the North Bridge which was in a state of dilapidation in 1830 and needed urgent repair. Twelve years later more extensive repairs were required to the south pier on the same side of the Bridge which required a protecting pier of facing, and other general repairs. Local architect Richard Sheppard, the county surveyor for the Northern Bridge District, prepared a specification of necessary repairs. The work, costing £150, was soon carried out.

In the winter of 1837, following the opening of the town's gasworks, the lights on the bridges were lit by gas instead of oil.

After the collection of tolls ceased, the Toll Houses were redundant. Initially it was proposed to demolish the one on the North Bridge, but in 1838 it was sold to Miss Beaty. A condition of the sale was that 'it is occupied as a Private House and is not used or occupied as a Beer house, or other Public House and no noxious Trade or Business be used or exercised therein'.

The prosperous coaching era came to an end with the opening of the London to Birmingham Railway in 1838 which virtually ended the coaching trade overnight. By 1840 the number of coaches passing through the town had dropped from thirty to four. The number of people employed in horse-related trades must also have fallen sharply, but the 1851 census records a population of 3,651, which included 12 ostlers and 23 grooms and horse keepers in the town. Related trades flourished, with 17 blacksmiths, nine coach-makers, three coach-smiths, and eight wheelwrights.

With the death of Miss Beaty, the Toll House on the North Bridge and much of her property was bequeathed to local solicitor William Bateman Bull. He applied for, and was granted, permission to be allowed to make an opening, which is still in use, in the North Bridge wall near the old Toll House for the purpose of making a road into the field adjoining.

The Trustees employed Benjamin Taylor as their surveyor, for providing materials, keeping the roads in repair, lighting the lamps, and collecting rent from Trustees' property. His salary in 1855 was £33 10s. per annum. In 1860 the Trustees independently ordered stone from Mountsorrel, Leicestershire, which must have been transported by canal for the repair of 100 yards of the carriage way on the north side of Tickford Bridge. This became an annual order; as a result, Mr Taylor's salary was reduced to £20 a year.

In 1865 the death of an 11-year-old boy was reported in the local newspaper; he had fallen from the Tickford Bridge and drowned. In 1868 the paper reported that, following several tragic drownings, lifebuoys with 90-foot ropes, pole drags of 18 feet 6 inches long and rope drags of 50 feet long had been provided. One was set in Mrs Paybody's shoeing shop premises near Iron Bridge, one set in the cemetery against the National School wall, another was set on the lower walk near the mound at junction of the rivers, and another set close to the Bathing Place in Midsummer Holme – all were under the supervision of the Superintendent of Police.

With the loss of the coaching trade the town sought to increase its income by being connected to the railway network. Following a public meeting, the Newport Pagnell Railway Company was established in 1863. The line of the unprofitable Newport Pagnell Canal was purchased and its route was used for the railway line which opened for goods in 1865 and passengers in 1867. However, this branch line from Wolverton to Newport Pagnell did little to increase road traffic. That same year a new surveyor, Henry Rose, was appointed by the Trustees at a salary of £14 per annum paid quarterly. His job description was:

> Generally to superintend the Bridges and the Approaches thereto to the extent for which the Trustees are liable for repair, to scrape the road when required and to sweep down and keep down the road and pathway. To lay down and spread materials necessary for keeping the roads in repair, to rake in ruts and keep the surface level.

A responsibility assumed by the Trustees was the cleaning out of the river downstream from Tickford Bridge to the confluence of the Ouse and Lovat. They took this work so seriously that they contributed £5 towards the cost of a mud boat on the condition that the boat was considered their property. However, wealthy local landowners, Messrs Tyringham, Massey, Knapp and Eve, were allowed to use it when required on payment of a small charge.

The road over the North Bridge, being on a causeway, with stone revetment walls either side, was fairly well protected against subsidence. However, the approaches to the Tickford Bridge had deteriorated so much that in 1871 they were repaired with 50 tons of stone from Hartshill, Warwickshire, costing £20, and which probably now came to the town by rail.

In the early days of the telephone service in the town, the Trustees received an application from the Post Master General to erect telegraph posts on the North

Bridge in 1871. The Trustees inspected the position in which it was proposed to place the posts and were of opinion that:

> It is not desirable they should be placed on their Bridges. They suggested that a shorter and cheaper route for the Telegraph wires would be from the present Telegraph post near Mr Eve's mill and the meadow up to the Bridge in Lathbury at the commencement of the Sherington Road.

When the Tickford Bridge was first built it was flanked on the Tickford side by wooden fences, later replaced with iron railings on both sides of the road. On the Newport side there was a stone wall on the upstream side of the road and a wooden fence replaced with iron in 1820 on the downstream side. The railings on the Newport side were replaced by a stone wall, and later in 1874 the railings, on the east side on the Tickford End of the bridge, were also replaced. The new wall, which would reduce the erosion of the road surface, was built with new paving adjacent to it in 1876 by local builder James Coverley at a cost of £37 4s. The Trustees, the Feoffees of Town Lands and the County Surveyors of Highways shared the cost, each paying one third. After this, the Trustees granted the tenancy of the ground (actually the old road) between the new wall and the way to the old ford, to John Mitchell, the tenant of the Toll House by the bridge.

The population of the town had remained around 3,800 for some years, and the townsmen sought to increase their economy by attracting new industry and business. It was considered that being at the end of a branch line, from the London and North Western Railway at Wolverton, was not conducive to expansion. In the 1860s and 1870s the townsmen sought an extension of the railway from Newport Pagnell to Olney, which would have created a link with the Midland Railway. Although a bridge was erected across the green, and ground works were started in Bury Field and further along the route, the project eventually failed.

Vandalism on the bridges now began to occur and in July 1881 notice boards were placed on both bridges to caution people from damaging the bridges or throwing stones or materials which were the property of the Bridge Trustees.

The cost of road repairs was becoming increasingly difficult for the Trustees to fund as their main source of income was from their rented properties only. In 1884 they sought help from the County, requesting that an allowance be made towards the maintenance and repairs of 200 yards of highway at the

Tickford Bridge and 200 yards at the North Bridge. An answer was not readily forthcoming and correspondence on this issue continued for some time.

Eventually, with some input from the County, the job of the Trustees' surveyor became less involved, and in July 1886 they appointed local builder, John Shelton, to become road surveyor on a part time basis at £11 per annum.

AN UNSUCCESSFUL TRAMWAY TO OLNEY

The businessmen of the town were disappointed with the failure of the proposed railway to Olney. As an alternative they called a public meeting, held in January 1887, to consider a scheme for a steam tram service from the town to Olney. Subsequently, the Newport Pagnell Tramway Company was formed. However, the construction of this line was the beginning of considerable worry and work for the Trustees which ultimately led to their demise.

A condition of the permission granted for the tramway was that the river bridges along the route were to be widened. The work was to be carried out at the expense of the tramway company, to allow the everyday traffic to continue alongside the trams. The company was not happy about this and claimed the Bridge Trustees were being obstructive and wanted the north bridges rebuilt with no cost to them.

Work started on laying the tramlines from Newport Pagnell station through the High Street towards the North Bridge early in 1888. In June the Bridge Trustees requested plans of the proposed widening of the bridge and, having inspected them, were unanimously of the opinion that the proposed method of carrying out the tramways on the approaches to the bridge was not consistent with the requirement of public safety. They requested a meeting on the subject with an officer of the Board of Trade before coming to any decision. The plans were soon revised and presented to the Trustees by the tramway engineer and Mr Edward Swinfen Harris of Stony Stratford, who was the County Bridge Surveyor. After the meeting the Trustees agreed that Mr Harris be employed as their Consulting Engineer or Surveyor.

At a subsequent meeting, the promoters of the Tramway Company agreed to carry out the necessary widening of the North Bridges in stonework by means of granite corbels and arches where necessary, so that the roadway was 22 feet 6 inches, and the footway was four feet wide. The plan and method of construction was approved by Mr Harris who was acting as advising architect to the Bridge Trustees.

However, later in November 1888, Mr Harris and Mr Sellon, the Tramway Company engineer, met the Trustees to consider further revised plans, using hollow iron corbels. These were accepted and left in the hands of Mr Harris to be carried out to his satisfaction.

The bridges were widened on their west side to carry new parapet walls. The widened roadway and new parapet wall of the north bridge was supported by an arch, above the original arch, flanked by a blind arch on each side (*see* Fig. 4). The new arch was carried on heavy iron corbels inserted into the old bridge. The keystone (*see* Fig. 3) of this new central arch was dated 1890. The final width of the roadway, including the footpaths over both the North and Middle bridges, was 27 feet.

By July 1890 the Trustees had complained to the Tramway Company about the unnecessary delay in completing the work, presumably the laying of the rails on the bridges, as they, in consequence, had been unable to repair the roadway which was becoming seriously damaged. The Tramway Company was by now in financial difficulties. Two years later the County Council, having doubts about the future of the Tramway Company, issue an ultimatum. If the work was not completed by 1 June 1893 it would take up all the lines already laid, repair the road surfaces and recoup the cost from the sale of the Tramway Company's stock of granite sets, rails, and other materials.

The Tramway Company did not meet this deadline; it failed because the Board of Trade prevented the line from running through the village of Emberton. The Company, not having the powers of compulsory purchase, was unable to purchase land for a bypass route and subsequently went into bankruptcy.

The County Surveyor then took up the rails and sought tenders for their purchase. The cost of removal of the materials and for making good roadways came to £618 7s. 10d. The full amount was never received since the Tramway Company and the London and General Bank, which had supported them, both went into liquidation.

The Trustees were concerned about these events. They had experienced several years of disruption and, to add to this, had to purchase an additional 25 tons of granite to make good their roads.

THE HANDOVER OF THE BRIDGES TO BUCKINGHAMSHIRE COUNTY COUNCIL

All of this had been a headache for the Trustees. As early as July 1890 they discussed the desirability of handing over the whole of their property to the Buckinhamshire County Council.

The following letter was sent to all Trustees:

NEWPORT PAGNELL
17th July 1890

Sir,

Meeting of the Bridge Trustees will be held at the Clerk's Office at Newport Pagnell, on THURSDAY, the 24th Day of JULY INSTANT, at Eleven o'clock in the Forenoon, when your attendance is requested –

To discuss the desirability of handing over the whole of
the property belonging to the Bridge Trustees to the Bucks County Council.

Yours faithfully,

CHARLES W. POWELL, Clerk to the Trustees

The matter was deferred for further consideration and advice sought from the Local Government Board as to whether an Act of Parliament needed to be obtained to enable the Trustees to carry out their plan to hand over the whole of their property, together with all rights and duties of the Trustees, to the Council, and whether the transfer could be carried out without expense to the Trustees by the Local Government Board.

Local County Councillor, Thomas Taylor, a member of the Highways Committee of Buckinghamshire County Council, had already brought up the possibility of a County takeover at its meeting on 2 March 1893. He had enquired as to whether the Committee would recommend the full Council to take over the Newport Pagnell Bridges, and on what terms. Mr Taylor stated that the property belonging to the Bridges Trust was just about sufficient to maintain the bridges and that the Bridge Trustees would be prepared to transfer all of the property to the Committee if the Committee would take over.

Subsequently, in May 1893, the Highways Committee recommended to the County Council that the bridges should be taken over as County Bridges, provided it could be arranged without loss to the County, and that the Local Government Board sanctioned the transfer by Provisional Order or otherwise.

The accounts of the Bridge Trustees were submitted to the County and showed that the income of the property was more than sufficient to maintain the bridges.

As a result the Committee commissioned a report on the condition of the Tickford Bridge. This was carried out by a Mr Bagally, whose report drew attention to the poor condition that the bridge had been left in by the Gas Company after putting pipes across the bridge, and by the Rural Sanitary Authority after it had put water mains across the bridge. Local builder William Coverley was authorised to carry out, without delay, repairs required for the masonry of the North and Tickford bridges, as recommended in Mr Bagally's report.

However, the work on the Tickford Bridge was to be left until the spring of 1904. Now, for the first time in its life the Tickford Bridge, having been thoroughly surveyed, was subject to weight restrictions. It was resolved that the following notice respecting traction engines passing over the Tickford Bridge be fixed upon the approaches to the Bridge:

NOTICE
This Bridge is insufficient to carry
Weights beyond the ordinary traffic of
The district and owners of Traction or
Other engines will be held responsible
For and will have to make good any
Damage caused to the Bridge pursuant
To Sections 6 and 7 of the 24 and 25
Victoria chapter 70
By Order of the Newport Pagnell Bridge
Trustees.
Charles W Powell, Clerk

At a special meeting held at the Clerk's Office, Newport Pagnell, on 15 May 1895, the Trustees resolved:

That having considered the substantial repairs needed to put the Bridges and their approaches into a satisfactory state and the undesirability of re-instating the Tolls to raise the funds this meeting resolves to petition the Buckinghamshire County Council to take over the Bridges and their approaches, the other property, and all funds held by the Bridge Trustees subject to all existing liabilities.

Letters between the two bodies were exchanged. The County Council Surveyor was required to re-inspect and report on the bridges. The report dated 4 July 1895 stated that the bridge was in fairly good condition, but was sadly in need of cleaning and painting. However, the surveyor considered that some of the iron plates carrying the roadway might prove too light for heavy traffic and would necessitate the substitution of steel plates.

The Highways sub-committee now requested the full council to act on their resolution of 11 May 1893 and to complete arrangements for the taking over of the bridges. Negotiations continued and it was not until 30 September 1897 that the bridges finally became the property of the County Council.

The wheels of local government turn slowly, but delays in the handover were largely caused by the even slower action of the Trustees. March 1896 saw the County Council write to the Local Government Board to enquire as to whether any steps had been, or were being, taken on the part of the Bridge Trustees to obtain a Provisional Order or otherwise with a view to carrying out the proposal for handing over the bridges and bridge property to Buckinghamshire County Council.

The Trustees were clearly dragging their feet, as if reluctant to hand over the bridges and their property. It was not until April 1896 that a draft agreement was drawn up and October before a final version was agreed and a copy sent to the Local Government Board.

Later in the year the question of the collection of rents of the property belonging to the Bridge Trust, which was to be transferred to Buckinghamshire County Council, was discussed. A draft scheme was prepared by the Charity Commissioners for the Town Lands Charity, affecting part of the income of the Bridge Trustees to be transferred to Bucks County Council, and was approved by the County. It was agreed that Sydney Nicholson, who had collected the rents of the Bridge Trustees' properties would continue to do so on behalf of Bucks County Council pending a permanent arrangement

On 30 September 1897 the bridges became County Council property. Immediately, the County, in accordance with recommendations of the County surveyor, set about putting the roadways and footpaths into thorough order, repairing the bridges and erecting a store, on the bridge property, for the main road tools etc. The cost of this work was not to exceed £500, and, if practicable, a sufficient amount of the investments transferred to the Buckinghamshire County Council by the Bridge Trustees was to be sold to provide the cost of carrying out the work.

The work on the footpaths was completed in 1897; the rough pebbles between the North Bridges being replaced with blue brick paving. The newly formed Newport Pagnell Urban District Council (UDC) was now given grants by the County for such work as scraping the road surfaces over the bridges and other minor jobs.

A house for the County Main Road Foreman and a tools store were built on the west side of Tickford Street near the Tickford Bridge, at the end of the row of cottages erected by the Bridge Trustees.

9

The Twentieth Century

In the dying years of the 19th century, the problems of motor vehicles, weight restrictions, and vandalism on the bridges began to appear in the Trustees' Minute Books. Children were becoming a nuisance, throwing stones in the river and climbing among the ironwork of the Tickford Bridge. The old Trustees had tried to solve this by removing the steps down to the river at the foot of the bridge. In 1899 the County Surveyor ordered that strands of barbed wire should be twisted around the lower portions of the girders of the bridge to prevent children from climbing there.

The same year the Urban District Council decided to provide two public urinals in the town, one near the Town Hall and the other by the Tickford Bridge. They enquired as to whether the County Council would sell a piece of land adjoining the bridge for the erection of the urinal. The site was on the upstream, Tickford Street, side of the bridge. The County refused the application since they anticipated that the ground would be required for another purpose. The Urban District Council then sought permission from the County Council and the Governors of Queen Anne's hospital to locate the urinal on the Newport side of the river – this was also refused.

A year later, in March 1901, the urinal had not been built and the Urban District Council requested permission to erect it on the strip of land on the opposite side of the bridge near the old bridge Toll House. This land was actually the former road leading to the old stone bridge. In May the following year, the County Surveyor approved the plans. Later in the year, the urinal, a typical cast-iron Victorian structure secured to the bridge wall on the Toll House side, was opened. The entry was through an opening in the guard wall and down a flight of steps.

Permission from the County Council to erect the urinal was subject to an annual payment to the County of 1s. and an undertaking by the Urban District

31 *The entrance to the Victorian urinal on Tickford Bridge.*

Council to remove the structure and make good to the satisfaction of the County Surveyor upon receiving three months' notice. Despite being aware that it was an important survival, the urinal was unfortunately removed by the Urban District Council in 1972; three years after the bridge itself had been saved by being scheduled as an Ancient Monument.

The County were soon keen to dispose of several of the properties they had acquired with the bridges. Permission for the sale of the old Toll House at

Tickford Bridge was obtained from the Local Government Board in April. It was sold by auction in 1902; the purchaser was the tenant Mr Mitchell, for £180. The County then sought to use the proceeds from the sale towards the cost of building a new tool store and cottage. Further property was for sale in April 1903, when the County sold the five cottages (*see* Fig. 17) in Tickford Street, which had been built by the Bridge Trustees, by auction for £285.

In 1899, the advent of the motor car and heavier vehicles caused the County Council to consider whether it was possible to restrict the speed of motor cars on highways.

With the increase in motor traffic the County, under Article IV of the Heavy Motor Cars Order, 1904, were able to introduce regulations prohibiting heavy motor traffic from passing over bridges in the County. In July 1905 a Mr J. Booth was awarded the contract to paint signs prohibiting heavy motor traffic on County bridges, at a price of £7 4s. for 12 signs. The maximum axle weight for vehicles passing over Tickford Bridge was set at six tons.

The road surfaces at this time were not sealed with tarmac and as the new motor vehicles passed through the town they threw up clouds of dust. This was such a nuisance to both shop and house owners that the County ordered a speed limit of six miles per hour through towns and villages.

An increase in heavy traffic caused concern about the safety of the Tickford Bridge. Since it was built, nothing had been done about strengthening it. The County Surveyor recommended that heavy steel plates should be placed on the roadway to increase its weight-bearing capacity. Quotations for this work were sought, and in October 1899 one from the Phoenix Foundry Company at £112 for half-inch steel buckle plates to be placed under the roadway over the bridge was accepted.

Although the work was not detailed in the Minute Books it was carried out in 1905. Local ironmonger Mr Reg Odell recalled working on the bridge at that time. Apparently John Odell, his father, had the contract for the work and Reg gave the following account at the public meeting about the bridge held in 1967.

> I am the only man alive who actually worked on the bridge. I helped fit the new 6ft x 3ft Steel plates (Plate 32) bolted with 4" and 5" bolts, which replaced the original Cast Iron Plate under the road surface. My job was to be under the bridge and catch the drills as they feel through. My father, John Odell, borrowed men, George Atkins, Tom Clerk, and Alfred Higgins, from Mr Jack Bailey the Blacksmith to help in this work. There were no ratchet braces in those days and the new steel plates were fitted right to the edge of the Bridge.

32 *Steel buckle plates, fitted in 1905, as revealed by strengthening work in 1976.*

Reg Odell's memory of events was not quite clear; when the road surface over the bridge was removed in July 1976, it was found that the plates only covered the original cast-iron deck plates and not the footpaths. The plates were in fact secured by heavy bolts pushed through from underneath which must also have been part of Odell's work.

Once the plates were in position they were covered with brick rubble and compacted hoggin which was rolled to form the road surface. A tarmac surface was not laid until *c.*1912-14. In the summer of 1905, after the strengthening work was completed, the bridge was repainted, but there is no record of the colour used.

Soon after this, telephone cables crossing the river were the first of many service connections to be strung alongside the bridge. Along Tickford Street, overhead telegraph poles were used up to Salmons and Sons Works, and in 1906 the service was extended to the Workhouse, Renny Lodge, in London Road.

Whilst the bridge itself was in good repair, the flank walls of the abutments on the St John Street side needed regular maintenance and were completely rebuilt in 1908 at an estimated cost of £20. These repairs carried out in the early years of the century put the bridge in good order for many years.

PROPOSALS FOR REMOVAL OF TICKFORD BRIDGE

The increase in motor traffic in the first half of the 20th century meant that a bypass for the town was discussed by the Urban District Council in the 1930s. The construction of such a road would have alleviated the need for road widening in the town. But it was not to be built until 1973.

As the century progressed, heavy motor traffic made it necessary for pedestrians to take care when crossing the bridge. This became increasingly hazardous by the 1950s, and those with little interest in the bridge as an historic monument, and who did not appreciate its attractive structure, began to call for its demolition. Claims were made that it was structurally unsafe for heavy vehicles, even though it had carried Centurion Tanks during the Second World War.

Throughout the country the post-war years saw much urban rebuilding in the name of progress. Whilst Newport Pagnell did not suffer from enemy action, it had experienced much neglect in the years between the First and Second World Wars. The Urban District Council, not wishing to be left behind, sought to redevelop the town and planned large-scale destruction of houses and shops.

It was argued that the proposed M1 motorway, due to open in 1959, would cause a considerable increase in traffic and was a good excuse for demolition and road widening. St John Street, the Tickford Bridge, and Tickford Street, the main route from the town to the motorway at Junction 14 on the London Road, were now the main targets.

Whilst their Victorian predecessors had sought to widen the Ram Corner and improve Cannon Corner, the Urban District Council, together with the County Council, now carried out road widening with the wholesale demolition of the east side of St John Street, part of Tickford Street, and the north side of the High Street from and including the Ram corner down to the North Bridge. Together with the excuse of improving access through the town to the motorway, they claimed to be redeveloping properties unfit for habitation.

Once the roads were widened, the only bottleneck was Tickford Bridge. In 1959 the Urban District Council decided (by nine votes to one) that it must be replaced. Prominent among the objectors to its presence was local councillor, Dr A.A. Clay, who claimed that there would soon be a fatal accident on the bridge, even though no-one in the town could remember one ever happening.

THE SUCCESSFUL CAMPAIGN TO SAVE THE BRIDGE

Although there were proposals to build a footbridge alongside the bridge, the County Surveyor, in 1966, was reluctant to support the suggestion, stating that he would rather replace the Iron Bridge.

The arguments to remove the Tickford Bridge intensified and eventually the Wolverton and District Archaeological Society (W&DAS), which had several members in the town, launched a campaign to save it.

In January 1967, Michael Harris, on behalf of the W&DAS, sought the support of the Council for British Archaeology (CBA) which successfully lobbied for the bridge, already listed as a Historic Building Grade III, to be raised to Grade II. The CBA were particularly interested in the rare Victorian urinal (*see* Fig. 31).

On 18 March 1967 the Ministry of Housing and Local Government advised the County Council and the Urban District Council that the bridge would receive protection by being raised to Grade II. Regardless of this the Urban District Council continued their efforts to get the bridge removed, supported by the County Highways Committee who believed that Government money would be more readily available for a new bridge than for a pedestrian footbridge to be built alongside it.

Early in July the Surveyor reported to the Urban District Council that any scheme for highways improvements should include the replacement of the Iron Bridge. The Urban District Council continued its relentless attack on the bridge and on 9 July 1967 passed a resolution, seven in favour and four against, to have the bridge removed. However, the County Surveyor was aware of the Preservation Society's attitude and envisaged the possibility of this decision being reversed when it came under pressure.

THE PUBLIC MEETING, 1967

In view of the Urban District Council's decision, five local people, Ray Bailey, John Coales, Newman Cole, Michael Harris and Dennis Mynard, all members

**IRON BRIDGE
NEWPORT PAGNELL**

A

Public Meeting

Will be held in the

Church House, Newport Pagnell

on Wednesday, July 19th, 1967

at 8 p.m.

**Any person interested in giving support towards preserving
the Iron Bridge is asked to attend.**

*33 The
poster for the
1967 meeting.*

of W&DAS, immediately called a public meeting, inviting any person interested in giving support towards preserving the Tickford Bridge to attend.

The meeting was held in the Church House, Newport Pagnell, on Wednesday 19 July 1967 at 8 p.m. and was attended by almost 150 people.

Mr Arthur Leary, a local councillor who was always deeply concerned with local issues, called the meeting to order at 8 p.m. and explained to the assembled crowd that he had been asked to take the chair by the organisers of the meeting. As there were no objections he remained in the chair throughout the meeting.

In his opening address, Mr Leary, as chairman, said that the object of the meeting was to see what support in the town there would be for the retention of the bridge. At the same time anyone present who was against this was earnestly asked to say so.

The meeting commenced with a brief historical outline of iron bridges by Michael Harris, which included a few details about the Tickford Bridge not generally known.

After this stage the Chairman asked three salient questions:

1. Was the bridge dangerous?
2. Would it cause loss of life?
3. Was it likely to collapse?

He believed it to be the safest place to cross the road since you could see both ways and, what was more important, you could also be seen. At the moment it was a limiting factor to the Tickford Street 'Race Track', but with the widening of the road this would extend up to the traffic lights.

The meeting was then declared open for questions.

Mr Newman Cole asked if there was any reason to believe the Bridge to be unsafe. The Chairman replied by saying he hoped it was safe. Councillor Mr Fred James stated he had known the bridge for 50 years, having played on it and under it as a boy. He declared that he had driven all types of vehicles over it and the County Authorities would never have asked the Local Authority to express their opinion if it had been unsafe. He felt that if the County thought it was dangerous it would have been removed years ago. The safety of pedestrians was the only major question and whilst foot bridges were a must, the answer for the town was a bypass.

The Chairman suggested that one footpath would be sufficient on the upstream side. The new school would be on this side, and people always had to cross the road somewhere.

Councillor A. Clay was the next speaker, saying he had come as an individual and not as a representative of the Urban District Council. This was not a problem that had suddenly arisen, nor was it a problem in isolation, but one that had been discussed by the Council many times.

There were three major problems so far as traffic in Newport Pagnell was concerned:

1. The proposed New City and expansion in North Buckinghamshire.
2. Tickford Street, in which the bridge was a Bottle neck.
3. High Street: The County Council had asked the Urban District Council for priorities and, as we all knew, the High Street had been nominated, before the development now taking place on the west side of Tickford Street was envisaged.

The County Surveyor had been told by the Urban District Council in December 1966 that the town wanted to keep the Tickford Bridge, but had suggested that if it were replaced it might give Tickford Street a higher priority.

Some time ago a petition had been organised by some of the residents of the Street, asking that the footpaths in this part of the town should be improved.

This was sent to the Member of Parliament to try to get something done, but, bearing in mind the County Council had 153 major road schemes in hand, the Urban District Council felt they should accept the opinion of the County Surveyor – that by including a new bridge in with the Tickford Street Scheme, there was a better chance of getting a higher priority for the widening of Tickford Street. If the bridge were retained the priority would be put back. It was dangerous as a traffic hazard and therefore a majority of the Urban District Council had decided regretfully that the County Council should do as they wished.

If the footpaths were removed and separate footbridges constructed, the bridge would still be seven feet short of the required width of 30 feet – it also needed to be considered whether the outer spans of the bridge were capable of carrying the heavy vehicles to the same degree as the inner span. If and when Britain joined the Common Market there would be far more and far larger lorries with trailers which would have to cross the bridge. Councillor Clay asked how many lives was the bridge worth. As an individual he would like the bridge kept, but as a councillor he could not risk the loss of a single life.

A prominent townsman, Mr Harold Hill Bailey, said he was disturbed about the Urban District Council policy regarding this old town. St John Street had been unnecessarily ruined as there was no doubt that Newport would have its bypass. Councillor Clay had spoken about the Tickford Bridge bottleneck but the Cannon Corner, High Street and North Bridges needed to be considered. If anything happens on the bridge it would be due to negligence – were the North Bridges therefore also unsafe? There was no reason at all to remove the bridge. Mr Bailey also felt that the proposed demolition opposite the church and the altering of the High Street would defer the bypass still further. Mr Bailey wanted an answer from Councillor Clay on the Council's decision.

Alderman W. Beesley, a member of the County Highways and Bridges Committee, said that at a meeting held on the previous Thursday it had been decided that the matter should rest in abeyance for the time being and no decision had been taken. When the master plan for Milton Keynes was produced it might be found that money had been spent unnecessarily. He thought that a footbridge, should one of these be put alongside the bridge, could be erected for about £6,000. He also pointed out that recently Marlow Bridge had been strengthened and thus preserved for posterity. The County Council were aware of the need to retain items of historical interest. He had spoken to Mr Franklin the County Surveyor, who said he would have come to the meeting if he had not had a prior engagement.

County Councillor, Mrs A.M. Durbridge, agreed with the previous speaker that the suggestion of a weight limit was one way of overcoming the problem, and that Cannon Corner was the main problem. The only real answer was a bypass which had been talked about for 30 years. The scheme for Milton Keynes would be out in two years, but before then the pattern of roads in the area would be clear. Newport needed a north-south and east-west bypass. She was in favour of keeping the bridge but at the same time agreed it was a severe pedestrian hazard, and as a bypass was a 'must', so were footbridges.

Mr Reginald Odell gave an interesting diversion, saying he believed he was the only man alive who had actually worked on the bridge in 1900. He suggested that concrete stanchions be put in the river supporting a footbridge.

Councillor Charlie Evans held the opinion that the problem of safety was a red herring, and he wanted the bridge inspected without delay to see if it was safe. The major problem was that of pedestrians. He thought Mr Bailey was right – there was no need to knock it down. After all the High Street is to be a pedestrian precinct and the matter can 'be summed up with one question – Do we want to retain the bridge? If the answer is yes, then let us raise the £6,000 locally to get a foot bridge erected, instead of waiting until the County Council has the money'. A bypass was the only firm solution.

The Chairman thought it was better just to say 'we want to keep it'.

Councillor Peter Jackson spoke next, saying he had been resident in Newport Pagnell for only two years, and when he was first elected to the Council he was given a brochure prepared by the Urban District Council depicting the bridge as the background to the Riverside Walk Scheme. He thought the bridge was symbolic of the town. A new brick-built bridge would not be in keeping. He had information that although the bridge may not have been surveyed recently, the Army did survey it and it carried 80-ton Centurion tanks up to 1956 at least.

Councillor Clay's argument about the Common Market and the large continental lorries and trailers was another red herring. Even when the tanks crossed the bridge it must have borne a distributed weight of at least 40 tons. What was wanted was a footbridge on one side and the bridge preserved. A plan for a new bridge produced by the County Surveyor proposed a 30-foot carriageway, with two 6-foot footpaths. The Urban District Council supported this, voting seven in favour and four against the proposal. The whole problem was that the County Council had no money for footbridges, but could find plenty for new road bridges.

Councillor A. Clay said he would like an answer to his question as to whether the bridge could carry the same weight at the edges as the centre.

Mr Fancutt replied by saying that the speed of an 80-ton tank over the bridge would have been carefully controlled and the effect on the bridge would be very different for a continental lorry and trailer. The Urban District Council should suggest that a severe speed restriction be enforced on both sides of the bridge. Hump-back signs would also help.

The Chairman said that it would appear to be the general opinion of the speakers that the Urban District Council had made a premature decision. There were five councillors present, so if there was a resolution from this meeting asking the Urban District Council to withdraw its decision until such time that a survey had been carried out, then no doubt those councillors present would see that such a resolution was discussed appropriately.

Mr Ray Bailey considered that if Marlow Bridge had been made safe then surely the bridge could be strengthened similarly and the heavy traffic carried. Alderman W. Beesley pointed out that no decision had actually been made by the County Council, and the Urban District Council would be kept informed. Councillor Clay stated that the County Highways and Bridges Committee had asked for the opinion of the Urban District Council as to whether the bridge should be retained or replaced. Alderman W. Beesley emphasised that this would only have been the County Surveyor seeking local advice for presentation to the Highways and Bridges Committee.

Finally the Chairman suggested a resolution worded as follows:

> This public meeting asks the UDC to withdraw its decision in respect of the demolition of the Tickford Bridge, until such time as a Surveyors' report is in the hands of the Council, and in the meantime there should be steps taken to provide footbridges for pedestrians.

Ray Bailey suggested that the proposed footbridge should harmonise with the design of the Tickford Bridge.

The meeting then voted on the Chairman's suggested resolution, 135 were in favour, two against, and there were four abstentions. The Chairman then declared the resolution carried and the meeting closed. Newman Cole proposed a vote of thanks to the Chairman for conducting the meeting, which was heartily endorsed.

After the meeting a report was produced which included the following summary by the Chairman:

> In summarising the opinions expressed at the meeting, it can fairly be said that the question of pedestrian safety was foremost in the minds of all, and the preservation of the bridge itself against such consideration was not sought by anyone present. There had been no fatalities on the present bridge, but could anyone given an undertaking that there would be no fatalities on a new Bridge?
>
> It was, however, generally felt that some pedestrian walk ways were needed in the form of footpaths on at least the upstream side of the Bridge, and these should be in keeping with the design of the present structure.
>
> The traffic problems on the bridge are really no different from those experienced on any of the major roads running through the town.
>
> It was the unanimous feeling of everyone present that the only solution to the traffic problem was the provision of the By-pass which had been under consideration for so many years. Any expenditure of a major character on the bridge would only push back the date for the commencement of the By-pass. It was unlikely that any further major road works would be carried out in and around Newport Pagnell until the new road pattern for the district had been established in conjunction with the plans for the Milton Keynes new City.
>
> It was premature of the Urban District Council to acquiesce in the demolition of the Tickford Bridge before having an Engineers' report on the safety of the structure, particularly in view of their stated desire to retain the bridge as an important feature of the Riverside walk development and as one of the characteristics of Newport Pagnell which makes it a pleasant and desirable place in which to live.
>
> Signed
> A. Leary Chairman 120 Tickford Street, Newport Pagnell.

THE TICKFORD BRIDGE SCHEDULED AS AN ANCIENT MONUMENT

Following the public meeting, Dennis Mynard, who worked as a Research Assistant at the Inspectorate of Ancient Monuments, and County Museum Curator Christopher Gowing, brought the bridge to the notice of Arnold Taylor, the Chief Inspector of Ancient Monuments. Arnold visited with several others and the bridge was subsequently scheduled as an Ancient Monument as a matter of some urgency.

The Scheduling of the Iron Bridge on 27 September 1967 took both the County Council and the Urban District Council by surprise. They were taken aback by the swift action of central government to protect the bridge. Within a few weeks the Urban District Council demanded instant action from the County to ensure the safety of the bridge. The response was to instruct their

34 The pedestrian footbridge on the west side of Tickford Bridge.

surveyor to carry out a new survey and assessment of its load-bearing capacity. This action set in motion further detailed studies of the bridge and a series of remedial works which took place over the next two decades.

Whilst the future of the bridge was now ensured, the unique Victorian cast-iron urinal came under threat and was destroyed. In March 1969 the Urban District Council advised the County Council that it was more economic to close the urinal than to spend money on expensive improvements. The County agreed and in October 1970 requested the Urban District Council to remove it; the work took place in 1972.

In 1971 the County Council decided to prepare a scheme for a footbridge, which was subsequently erected in 1973 on the west side of the bridge (*see* Fig. 34). The following year, masonry repairs were carried out on the bridge abutments by Spur Construction.

DAMAGE TO THE BRIDGE, 1973

In June 1973 a section of the railings on the east side of the bridge was seriously damaged by a lorry, when sections of the ironwork were broken and fell into the river.

Repair and restoration of the bridge was undertaken by Gomme's Forge of Loosley Row, Princes Risborough. The fallen section, weighing 15 cwt, was recovered from the river and taken to Gomme's Forge (*see* Fig. 35) for the work to be carried out. A pattern was carved in wood over which a mixture of sand and waterglass was poured to form a hollow mould. The process was repeated and the two moulds were joined together ready for the molten cast iron to be poured in. Iron was melted in a forge (*see* Fig. 36) and heated to about 1,700 degrees centigrade; once the molten metal was of a certain colour and viscosity the smiths poured it into the mould. When cool the mould was broken and the recast parts were welded to the sections of railing. The above is based on an article which appeared in the *Thames Gazette*, 4 September 1973.

The recast and repaired sections were then cleaned and refitted to the bridge in September. The quality of the work was such that they were virtually indistinguishable from the original sections (*see* Fig. 38).

In 1972 extensive restoration of the stonework, including some new cappings of Doulton stone, was carried out. Work was also undertaken to assess the condition of the ironwork which had suffered corrosion from water seeping through the decking. Evidence of some 16 coats of paint was found on the bridge, and it was established that the original colour had been a very dark grey.

35   (Above) Damaged section of railings awaiting repair at Gomme's Forge, Loosley Row, 1973.

36   (Below) Gomme's Forge, 1973.

37 *Graham and Geoffrey Baker, blacksmiths, pouring molten iron into the mould for repairing the sections of Tickford Bridge, 1973.*

38 The recast and repaired railings.

STRENGTHENING THE DECKING, 1976

Tests by the Ministry of Transport to assess the strength of the bridge had confirmed that it needed upgrading. Work took place in July to strengthen the decking. The road surface was removed, exposing the mild steel buckle plates (*see* Fig. 32) fitted over the original cast-iron plates in 1905. It was discovered that the buckle plates only covered the ribs of the bridge and not the footpaths at each side. Also revealed was the back of the fascia below the side railings and a mass of service pipes and cables, which fortunately had not been hung alongside the bridge.

39 *The eastern side of Tickford Bridge, showing the bottom of the cast sections of railing and the service cables and pipes, 1976.*

An elaborate system of strengthening was carried out. Longitudinal RSJs were place over the original ribs of the bridge; over these a layer of closed cell polyethylene was applied to absorb shocks. Next, a strong steel squared mesh was laid, over which concrete was poured, to form a reinforced concrete mat over the whole width of the bridge. Next, a smooth concrete layer was applied, onto which a waterproof membrane of fibre reinforced bitumen laminate topped with an aluminium foil was stuck down, the overlaps being sealed with bitumen. Finally, a tarmac road surface was laid over the bridge.

The work was carried out by Bletchley Construction Ltd, at a cost of just over £10,000. To date this has made a successful waterproof cover for the ironwork of the bridge.

Examination and assessment of the ironwork of the bridge took several years to complete. Delays occurred due to the slow decision-making of the various government bodies involved. During all of this time the County Council had to deal with enquiries and complaints from the Newport Pagnell Town Council and others about the progress.

In 1984 a survey of the ironwork revealed a lot of minor damage caused by water building up in hollow castings and loose joints, some of which over the years had been packed with all sorts of unsuitable materials. This had resulted in corrosion which had been painted over in the past, allowing further damage to take place. It took four years to get all parties involved to agree on the process to be used. Therefore, repairs were not undertaken until 1988, when many joints were cleaned out and filled with an epoxy resin matrix binder that was claimed to be stronger than steel and lighter than aluminium.

After the strengthening work the bridge was repainted in a very dark grey to match its original paintwork. In December 1987 the County put proposals for the repainting to English Heritage but were not given the go ahead to proceed for two years. The delay was mainly due to the requirement to find an acceptable scaffolding company. The painting finally commenced in October 1989 and was completed the following February.

WEIGHT RESTRICTIONS AND BOLLARDS

In June 1987 the bridge was declared to be unsafe by the Milton Keynes Transport and Highways Committee and as a temporary measure a weight limit of three tonnes, just over three imperial tons, was imposed. Despite warning signs some heavy lorries were still driven over the bridge.

This reckless behaviour caused the Council to erect bollards (*see* Fig. 40), leaving a carriageway width of only six feet six inches for vehicles to pass between them, in May 1998. As a result, some emergency vehicles were unable to cross the bridge and had to make a detour via the Milton Keynes grid roads. Buses were also unable to cross the bridge; some services were cut and others replaced by special minibuses hired by Milton Keynes Council.

The bollards were in place for over a year, during which time there were many complaints from owners of wide cars, four-wheel-drive vehicles, and vans. Numerous wing mirrors were broken and other damage caused as cars were driven through. There was also a serious accident when a driver lost control of his car and hit a bollard which crushed the passenger door. As a result the driver's wife was injured, trapped in the car, and had to be released by firemen from two stations; one on the town side of the bridge and the other at Broughton on the Tickford side of the bridge.

Clearly the bollards could not stay in place forever, and during 1998 remedial work using carbon fibre strengthening was proposed. Due to be carried out in February the following year, the commencement of the work was delayed due to unseasonable heavy rain and low temperatures. Eventually, the contractor, Topbond plc Group, carried out the work which was completed by the end of June. Subsequently, a final test confirmed the strengthening was successful and that the capacity of the bridge was upgraded to carry the continental 40 tonne vehicles.

The bridge was closed for two days (*see* Fig. 41) whilst the bollards and signs were removed. Normal traffic resumed when the bridge was reopened on Monday 28 June 1999 by local councillors.

After the above work the bridge was once again repainted in its original colour.

40 *Bollards and weight restriction signs on the Tickford side of the bridge.*

41 *The last day for the bollards, Sunday 27 June 1999.*

Upgrading to Listed Building Grade I, 2001

Paul Woodfield carried out a survey of historic buildings in Newport Pagnell for the Milton Keynes Council, with a view to upgrading certain buildings and listing others. As a result of this review, the bridge was awarded Grade I status. It was considered to be a foremost work of early cast-iron engineering and the only one surviving in near its original condition, still taking modern traffic.

Today the bridge stands (*see* frontispiece) as a monument of national importance in the history of civil engineering and the use of cast iron. Long may it carry traffic.

Appendix One:
Table of Temporary and Full Toll Charges

Temporary tolls were charged on the North Bridge from December 1809 to June 1810, the period when a temporary bridge linked the old and new bridges. After this full tolls were charged:

For every Coach, Berlin, Landau, Chariot, Calash, Chaise, or other such carriage drawn by four or more Horses or other Beasts of Draught
+ Temporary Toll nine pence
+ Full amount of Toll one shilling and six pence

As above but drawn by three or two horses or other Beasts of Draught
+ Temporary Toll six pence
+ Full amount of Toll one shilling

As above but drawn by only one horse or other Beast of Draught
+ Temporary Toll three pence
+ Full amount of Toll three pence and a half penny

For every Wagon, Wain, Dray Cart, Carr, or other such like carriage drawn by four or more Horses or other Beasts of Draught, for each Horse or other Beast of Draught
+ Temporary Toll two pence
+ Full amount of Toll three pence and a half penny

As above but drawn by three or two horses or other Beasts of Draught for each Horse or other Beast of Draught
+ Temporary Toll two pence
+ Full amount of Toll four pence

As above but drawn by only one horse or other Beast of Draught
+ Temporary Toll three pence
+ Full amount of Toll six pence

For every Horse, Mare or Gelding, Mule, or Ass laden or unladen and not drawing
+ Temporary Toll one penny
+ Full amount of Toll one and a half pence

For every Drove of Oxen, Cows or Neat Cattle per score
+ Temporary Toll two pence
+ Full amount of Toll four pence
+ And so in proportion for any greater or less number

For every Drove of Calves, Hogs, Swine or Sheep, or Lambs per score
+ Temporary Toll two and a half pence
+ Full amount of Toll five pence

On Sundays travellers paid double the normal rate.

Appendix Two:
Earlier Cast-Iron Bridges than the Tickford Bridge, which are still standing

1 ♦ THE IRON BRIDGE, COALBROOKDALE

The world's prototype iron bridge of 1775, a single arch of over 100-foot span over the River Severn, designed by T.F. Pritchard and cast by the Coalbrookdale Company.

Now used by pedestrians only. Notable for its use of carpentry-style joints which were never repeated. Two small-scale replicas were made for the landscape gardens of Wörlitz, East Germany, in 1799, and still exist.

2 ♦ PONT Y CAFNAU, GLAMORGAN

A 47-foot span 'A'-frame cast-iron bridge over the River Taff, designed by Watkin George in 1793, and cast by Cyfarthfa ironworks, Merthyr Tydfil. Carries minor traffic only.

3A ♦ COUND ARBOUR BRIDGE

Of 1797, designed by John Dodson and Telford, a segmental bridge spanning 36 feet, cast by the Coalbrookdale Company, on a minor road and used by light traffic, and its neighbour.

3B ♦ CANTLOP BRIDGE, SHROPSHIRE

A small road bridge, now bypassed, built in 1812 over the Cound Brook, probably designed by Telford, and built in 1797, spanning 32 feet.

4A AND B ♦ SYDNEY GARDENS BRIDGES, BATH

Two small canal bridges, of 23 foot- and 30-foot span, 10 feet wide over the Kennet and Avon Canal designed by John Rennie over the period 1794-1816. The bridges were made by the Coalbrookdale Company in 1800. They now survive for pedestrian use, and as public garden ornaments.

5 ✦ SPANISH TOWN BRIDGE NEAR KINGSTON, JAMAICA

Designed by Thomas Wilson in 1801 and cast by Samuel Walker & Co. of Rotherham, spanning 81 feet between high abutments over the Rio Cobre, on the main road into the then capital of the British colony. It is now used solely by pedestrian traffic, having been superseded by a modern bridge in 1931.

6 ✦ STRATFIELD SAYE, NORTH HAMPSHIRE

Designed by Thomas Wilson in 1802 and cast by Walkers of Rotherham for George Pitt (Lord Rivers), and spanning 40 feet over the River Loddon, on the southern approach to what became the Duke of Wellington's favourite abode, Stratfield Saye House. At 13 feet 6 inches wide, it now only takes internal estate traffic. It was restored in 1998-9 and received the National Historic Bridge Award in 2000.

7A AND B ✦ HELMINGHAM HALL, SUFFOLK

Two bridges of two spans of over 60 feet, over the moat at Helmingham, probably designed by John Adey Repton, the garden designer for Lord Tollemache in around 1804, and made by Ransomes of Ipswich. They now carry light estate traffic only.

Appendix Three:
List of Cast-Iron Bridges made before the Tickford Bridge

The following pages feature a comprehensive table, outlining a list of cast-iron bridges constructed or proposed before the Tickford Bridge. The table shows the location of the bridge; the river it crosses; the county or country it is located in; the date; number of spans; dimensions of the span or spans; the manufacturer; the designer; whether it was eventually built or not; and whether the bridge still exists today.

LOCATION	CROSSING	CO.	DATE	SPANS	SPAN	MANUFACTURER	DESIGNER	BUILT	EXISTS NOW
Lyon		France	Pre-1770	3	1 x 83ft			No	
Inverary	R. Aray	Argyll	1774	2	43ft		R. Mylne	?	Two bridges proposed
Coalbrookdale	R. Severn	Salop	1775	1	100ft 6in	Abraham Derby	T.F. Pritchard	Yes	Yes
Langholm		Scotland	1775-8	1		Davidson, Res. Engr	Thomas Telford		
Stourport	R. Severn	Worcs.	1775	1					
Buildwas	R. Severn	Salop	1795-6	1	130ft segmental	Coalbrookdale Co.	Thomas Telford	Yes	No, but remained in use until 1905
Coalport	R. Severn	Salop	1799-1818	1	103ft	Banks and Onions	John Onions	Yes	Replaced 1817 using some old parts
Raincy, Nr Paris			1788				Thos Blaikie (Scot)		Replica of Iron Bridge at Coalbrookdale on small scale
(Rotherham)			1787	1	90ft	Walkers, Rotherham	Tom Paine	Yes	No. Experimental single arch of four ribs
Philadelphia	R. Schuylkill	USA	1787	1	400ft		Tom Paine	No	No
Unknown site	Holland							No	No information
Syon Park	Parkland	Middlesex	1790	1			James Wyatt	No	For Duke of Northumberland
Island of Nevis		W. Indies	1791-4	1				No	Two others on record for Caribbean
Paddington		London	1792			Walkers of Rotherham			
Chirk Bridge	R. Dee	Powys	1793-4	1		Davidson, Res. Engr	Thomas Telford		
Longbridge		Salop	1793	1		Davidson, Res. Engr	Thomas Telford		
Worlitz, Magdeburg	Gardens	Prussia	1791	1				Yes	Yes. Copy of Coalbrookdale in W.I.

Location	Crossing	Co.	Date	Spans	Span	Manufacturer	Designer	Built	Exists Now
Sunderland	R. Wear	Co. Durham	1793-6	1	236ft x 32ft wide	Walkers Rotherham	R. Burdon et al	Yes	Destroyed in 1929
Breslau	R. Streigauer	Silesia	1795-6	1	5 ribs, 43ft	Royal Malpane Fdy	John Baildon (Scot)	No	Demolished in 1930s
Buildwas	R. Severn	Salop	1795-6	1	130ft segmental		Thos Telford	Yes	Replace by Telford in 1796; destroyed
Pont y Cafnau	R. Taff	Glamorgan	1793	1	47ft 'A' frame	Cyfarthfa Ironworks	Watkin George Engr	Yes	Yes. Water trough and pedestrian
Stoke on Trent	Water feature	Staffs.	1794		c.110ft		Scheme only	Yes	Fragmentary. For the Marquis of Stafford
Stanford Court	R. Teme	Worcs.	1795				John Nash	Yes	Collapsed soon after erection
Gr Bolas		Staffs.	1795			M. Davidson, Res. Engr	Telford		[FROM HERE, MINOR BRIDGES
Bridgnorth	R. Severn	Salop	1795				Thos Telford		BY TELFORD EXCLUDED]
Sheffield	R. Don	Yorks.	1795		Small footbridge		?	No	Destroyed by flood 1864
Longdon-on-Tern Aqueduct	R. Tern	Salop	1796	4	47ft 'A' frame		Thos Telford	Yes	Yes. Disused since 1944
Chirk Aqueduct	R. Ceiriog	Clwyd	1796-1801		40ft spans	W. Hazeldine, Bridgnorth	Thos Telford	Yes	Yes, reinforced 1870
Pontcysyllte Aqueduct	R. Dee	Clwyd	1796-1805	19	44ft 6in	W. Hazeldine, Bridgnorth	Jessop/Telford	Yes	Yes, four ribs to each arch
Avington	In park	Hants.	1802		20ft			Yes	
Holmes Aqueduct	Derby Canal	Derbys.				? Butterley Co.	B. Outram		
Stanford	R. Teme	Worcs.	1797			Coalbrookdale Co.	Nash's 1797 patent	Yes	Second bridge survived to 1911
Bridgwater, first bridge	R. Parrett	Somerset	1797	1	75ft	Coalbrookdale Co.	T. Gregory	Yes	No, replaced, 1883

Location	Crossing	Co.	Date	Span	Spans	Manufacturer	Designer	Built	Exists Now
Cantlop	Cound Brook	Salop	1797	1	40+- segmental	?	?	Yes	Yes
Cound Arbour	R. Tern	Salop	1797	1	36ft segmental	Coalbrookdale Co.	John Dodson/ Telford	Yes	Oldest still in highway use
London	R. Thames	London	1797	1	600ft x 65ft rise	?	Telford & Douglas	No	–
Bath, Sydney Gdns	Kennet-Avon Canal	Avon	1800	2 bridges	23ft & 30ft	Coalbrookdale Co.	Charles Rennie	Yes	Two bridges, costing £228 each
Rhyd-y-car	R. Taff	Glamorgan	1800	1			Watkin George Engr	No	Dismantled 1970, re-erected
Pont d'Austerlitz	R. Seine	Paris	1800-6		105ft		Lamande	Yes	No, demolished, 1854
Spanish Town	Rio Cobre	Jamaica	1801		81ft x 15ft wide	Walkers of Rotherham	Thomas Wilson	Yes	Yes, cost £4,000
Menai Strait	Menai Strait	Gwynedd	1801-2	3	450ft/ 350ft/ 350ft		Charles Rennie	No (too costly)	
Paris, Pont des Arts	R. Seine	France	1802-4	9	Total 155m	English design	L-A de Cessart	Yes	Rebuilt in seven spans, 1981-4
Paris, Pont d'Austerlitz	R. Seine	France	1802-5	5	5ft x 106ft		L-A de Cessart	No	Replaced in stone, 1854
Stratfield Saye	R. Loddon	Hants.	1802	1	40ft	Walkers, Rotherham	Thos Wilson	Yes	Yes, in park. 13ft 6in wide
Stourport	R. Severn	Worcs.	1802-8	1		W. Hazeldine, Bridgnorth		No	Replaced, 1870
Staines	R. Thames	Middlesex	1802-3		179ft 9in	Walkers, Rotherham	Thos Wilson	Yes	No, cost £5,660
Norwich, St Miles Bridge	R. Wensum	Norfolk	1804	1	36ft 2ins segmental		James Frost, Norwich	Yes	Yes, only pedestrians
Helmingham park	Moat	Cambs.	1804-	2 no.	6ft oval?	Ransomes of Ipswich	John Nash?	Yes	Yes

Location	Crossing	Co.	Date	Span	Spans	Manufacturer	Designer	Built	Exists Now
Yarm	R. Tees	Teesside	1803-5		179ft 9ins	Walkers Rotherham	Thos Wilson	Yes	Fell down, 1806
Ballochindrain	R. Glendaroch	Argyll	1805-11				Thos Telford		
Tongland	R. Dee	Kirkubcudb	1805-8			A. Blane, Res. Engr	Telford and Nasmith	Yes	Cost £7,210
Carshalton	R.Wandle	Surrey	1805-6	1				No	Replaced c.1914
Dunkeld	R.Tay	Perthshire	1805-9				Thos Telford	Yes	No, cost £30,000
Urquhart, Old Spey Br	R.Spey	Moray	1806	3			Thos Telford	Yes	No, replaced after floor, 1852
Eglinton Tournament	Lugdon Water	Ayrshire	1807-11	3	102ft		David Hamilton	Yes	No
Wick	Wick Water	Sutherland	1805-7				Thos Telford		No
Bristol	Avon	Avon	1806			Coalbrookdale Co.	William Jossup		
Bristol		Avon	1806-7			Coalbrookdale Co.	William Jossup		
Town Bridge, Boston	R.Witham	Lincs	1807	1	86ft	Walkers of Rotherham	Rennie	Yes	Replaced 1913, two survive
Brentwood	parkland	Middlesex	1809				John Rennie		For Earl St Vincent
Linlathlen	Dighty Water	Dundee	c.1810			Unknown		Yes	Yes, Estate Bridge
Newport Pagnell	R. Gt Ouse	Bucks.	1810	1	58ft	Walkers, Rotherham	Thos Wilson	Yes	Yes
Robertstown Tramway	R. Cynon	Glamorgan	1811	Level	36ft 8in	Aberdare Tram Co.		Yes	Yes, oldest rail bridge in the world
Wolverton Iron Trunk	R. Gt Ouse	Bucks.	1809-11	2	2ft x 55ft	Ketley Ironworks	William Jessop	Yes	Yes

Bibliography

Brown, S.F., *The Old iron bridge, Spanish Town*, University of Kingston, Jamaica

Harris, M P., *Newport Pagnell's Iron Bridge*, Wolverton and District Archaeological Journal, 1 (1968), 60-63

Hassel, J., *A tour of the Grand Junction Canal*, London (1819)

Humber, W., *A Practical Treatise on Cast and Wrought Iron Bridges and Girders* (1857)

Labrum, E.A., *Civil Engineering Heritage, Eastern and Central England*, Thomas Telford Ltd, London (1994)

Peters, P.J., *Tickford Bridge Newport Pagnell. Report on Repair and Protection Works of 1989*, Buckinghamshire County Council Report, unpublished

Pevsner, N. and Williamson, E., *Buckinghamshire, Buildings of England Series*, 2nd edition (1994), 578

Smiles, S., *Lives of the Engineers* (1874)

Trinder, B. and Cossons, N., *The Iron Bridge*, Phillimore (2002)

Wright, N., *Boston: A Pictorial History*, Phillimore (1994)

The regional volumes of *Civil Engineering Heritage*

Individual papers in the annual Proceedings of the Institution of Civil Engineers

Index

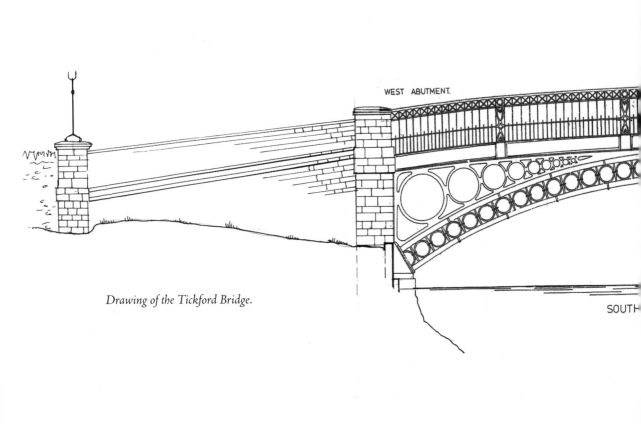

WEST ABUTMENT.

SOUTH

Drawing of the Tickford Bridge.